NEW GEOGRAPHY 1966-67

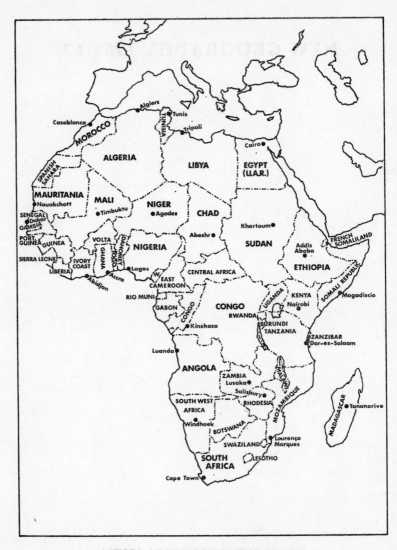

AFRICA AT THE BEGINNING OF 1967

NEW GEOGRAPHY
1966–67

John Laffin

Illustrated with maps

ABELARD-SCHUMAN

London   New York   Toronto

By the same author

Return to Glory
Middle East Journey
One Man's War
Digger: Story of the Australian
   Soldier
Scotland the Brave: Story of the
   Scottish Soldier
The Face of War
British Campaign Medals
Codes and Ciphers

Swifter than Eagles: Biography of
   Marshal of the R.A.F. Sir John
   Salmond
Anzacs at War
Jackboot: Story of the German
   Soldier
Boys in Battle
Links of Leadership
The Hunger to Come
etc.

© John Laffin
First published 1967
LCCC No. 67–14202

LONDON
Abelard-Schuman
Limited
8 King Sreet WC2

NEW YORK
Abelard-Schuman
Limited
6 West 57 Street

TORONTO
Abelard-Schuman
Canada Limited
896 Queen Street West

Abbreviations used in this book include:

HEP	Hydro-electric Power
TEE	Trans-European Express
NATO	North Atlantic Treaty Organisation
EFTA	European Free Trade Association
EEC	European Economic Community (The Common Market)
NCB	National Coal Board (Britain)
COMECON	Council for Mutual Economic Assistance (Eastern Europe)
AID	Agency for International Development (U.S.A.)
OPEC	Organisation of Petroleum Exporting Countries
m	million
sq m.	square mile
U.S.	United States (of America)
LAFTA	Latin American Free Trade Association
ECSC	European Coal and Steel Community (the Common Market countries)
UNESCO	United Nations Educational, Scientific and Cultural Organisation
WHO	World Health Organisation
FAO	Food and Agriculture Organisation

The information and statistics given in this book are correct to October 31, 1966.

To all geographers, from whom I would
appreciate criticisms and comments.

Herstmonceux   John Laffin
Sussex.

CONTENTS

7

Contents

Contents

Contents

Contents

Contents

LIST OF ILLUSTRATIONS

ABOUT THIS BOOK

One of the most serious drawbacks to modern knowledge is the lack of reliable *current* information about geographical matters. I use "geographical" in its broadest sense to cover physical, human, economic and all other aspects of a very wide subject. This book is a serious effort to supply up-to-date information, which is necessary for students at all levels of education, for teachers and instructors, for businessmen and for the many thousands of general readers who try, generally in vain, to keep track of world affairs and geographical developments. I am in a position to know about the difficulties involved because I not only teach geography but write for newspapers and magazines about current affairs.

As UNESCO has stated:*

> Geography is a subject that calls for the fullest possible documentation alike for those who teach it and for the pupils who study it. Hence teachers need to keep themselves permanently abreast of the progress of geographical science and of everything which can supplement their professional training. . . . What they learned at the teacher training college or the university cannot be regarded as anything more than the first step in their apprenticeship and they would quickly fall into a stultifying routine if they did not constantly seek to add to their knowledge.

Adding to my own knowledge involves me in hours of reading each day. To keep abreast of changes and progress I have found it necessary to subscribe to dozens of magazines, to read the bulletins of scores of official bodies, banks and government departments and to keep elaborate files and a card index system. However, my book is no mere collection of snippets from hand-outs. I have verified each reference with at least

* In *Source Book for Geography Teaching*.

two other sources. I have been particularly careful to check any information from government sources, for a country, not unnaturally, is apt to glorify its achievements. Some of these achievements, I have found, exist only on paper or in the imagination of publicity officials. Neither is my book a collection of statistics. Figures in tabular form are nothing more than bones and of very limited interest.

To avoid tedium, and to make reference a simple matter, I have been selective in my material. The basis of my selection has been simple enough, since throughout the preparation of the book I had in mind the presentation of material likely to be important to students facing examinations, at all levels. The actual material within the entries I have assessed and selected according to its general interest and educational value. I have been particularly careful to include important matters which have had little or no general publicity. Some of the most vital developments are disclosed only in specialist journals and would thus have little currency but for this book.

Obviously, people's ideas of what is important will differ, so it is possible that some readers may feel that a particular item should have been mentioned, especially if it should happen to have occurred in their own locality. Generally, unless an aspect of new geography has a national or an international interest or influence I have not included it. For instance, it does not seem important that in a recent year Rumania exported 6,354·1 thousand square metres of window glass or that the rail passenger service between Haltwhistle and Alston is to be maintained. To include a mass of similar information would merely muffle the significance of more important information.

To cover world-wide geography in all its aspects the accounts in this book must necessarily be terse and not discursive. Even so, I have commented at points where comment seems essential. Matters of purely political interest are outside the scope of *New Geography*, but where politics are related to economic geography—such as in the case of Rhodesia's Unilateral Declaration of Independence—then naturally they are included.

Naturally, most developments take place in the field of

economic geography, using the term in a very wide sense to include the business of *living*. As UNESCO has said:*

> Of all school subjects Geography is perhaps the best suited to bring about . . . understanding, concerned as it is with civics, patriotism, and the information essential to a knowledge and appreciation of other lands and national groups. Geography can show not only how other peoples have lived and are living, but also what they have contributed to the common heritage of mankind; most important of all it can demonstrate that despite political divisions the inhabitants of the earth are becoming increasingly interdependent in their economic and cultural relations. . . . The problems that have to be solved to provide men with food, to supply them with water in sufficient quantity and of good enough quality, to educate them and to give them more scientific knowledge, grow daily greater.

New Geography is not intended to replace textbooks: it would need to be of encyclopaedic length to do this. As *new* geography it is intended to supplement existing textbooks and especially those parts of them dealing with economic and human geography. Obviously, there can be no comparable change in physical geography, though aspects of physical geography are discussed in this book.

All geography textbooks are inevitably out of date—even this one!—if only because of the time lapse between completion of the manuscript and publication of the book. In many cases this is not surprising, for geography is a living subject, though "bursting with life" might be a better way to describe its development since 1945. But I have textbooks on my shelves, produced in 1966, in which some figures are twenty years out of date. There can be no excuse for this.

The publishers hope to bring out *New Geography* every two years, so that the edition for 1968–9 will obviously deal with developments since 1966–7. However, with this first edition I am considering developments mostly since 1963 or 1964, unless

* *Source Book for Geography Teaching.*

otherwise stated. In short, in the case of important developments I have gone back a little further than I would normally do, so as to collect the "threads" together.

To quote UNESCO again:*

> In economic geography a change is called for in the methods of graphical representation followed in textbooks. Instead of giving only curves that show merely the course of phenomena in the past, there should be no hesitation about projecting them with a different kind of line, for ten or perhaps twenty years in to the future on the basis of the foreseeable prospects.

In keeping with UNESCO thought, I have not only given the current figures, but, where possible the rate of increase. For instance, the annual increase of the sheep population of Australia is one million. For human populations I have been able to project figures to what they will be at the beginning of 1967. This is quite simple, as the population rate of increase is accurately known for nearly all countries, and records are kept by the United Nations. I have done this from a sense of frustration—experienced by many geographers—at so often finding in new books population figures that are years out of date.

The book is, I think, palatable, interesting and easy to use. All subjects are alphabetically listed. Generally, I have thought it better to deal with a country as a whole but occasionally I have dealt with an area (e.g. Alsace), commodities (sugar) or industries (fishing). Cross references from country to commodity and vice versa will enable any reader to acquire readily a complete picture of his particular immediate interest.

It is possible that a reader will find a country or subject in which he is interested not listed at all in this book. This is because it would be a waste of space to publish information already available. The prime purpose of *New Geography* is to present *new* geography. Consequently, a rapidly progressive country such as Australia is dealt with at length.

* *Source Book for Geography Teaching.*

About this Book

UNESCO states:*

For geography to achieve . . . liveliness of interest a further need is for textbooks and schoolbooks to concentrate more on setting out the vital problems—those which are of fundamental concern to regions and countries in relation to the production of foodstuffs and to physical and human phenomena.

This book does set out vital problems.

* *Source Book for Geography Teaching.*

MAJOR INFLUENCES

Any work claiming to be an account of new geography must draw attention to the major influences at work in the world. The most profound of these are the twin problems of hunger and over-population. Both have had far-reaching consequences and in the future will cause even greater changes in human and economic geography. The gap between the haves and the have-nots is steadily widening, as the former increase their agricultural, pastoral and industrial productivity while the latter increase only their populations.

World food production is increasing by about 1% yearly, but population by more than 2% (in 1965). Whatever we do now the world's population will have doubled by A.D. 2000. Man's survival depends upon his ability to control his rate of increase.

"Time is not on the side of those who would allow populations to take their course," D. K. Faris of the U.N. Technical Assistance Administration has written. "The growing restlessness of populations in the less developed nations becomes more understandable. We are teetering on the edge of calamity unlimited.... No nation can escape the threat posed by the pressure of skyrocketing populations on already inadequate food supplies, meagre industrial development, rampant illness and overwhelming ignorance."

But Ritchie Calder, Professor of International Relations, Edinburgh University, has given a pointer towards methods of coping with the increase. "It will need the combined intelligence and efforts of mankind to increase yields, recover the deserts, extend cultivation into climatically inhospitable regions and to farm the oceans which cover seven-tenths of our globe."

Hunger and population are dealt with alphabetically, but not so readily classifiable is another phenomenon of modern times—the drift of peoples to the cities. This can be noticed in almost every country in the world, and it is partly a revolt against what people—especially younger people—consider to be the fewer opportunities, the lower standards of living and the less interesting work of the country. In addition there is the very real unemployment and near starvation of the countryside. The trend is specially evident in Latin America, where hundreds of thousands are moving to the cities each year. Of Latin America's 225m people 45% now live in the cities. Four of the world's 13 largest cities are in Latin America: Buenos Aires (7m); Mexico City (5m); São Paulo (4·4m); Rio de Janeiro (3·7m). Ten Latin American cities have populations of more than 1m and by 1980, according to United Nations estimates, 16 others will have 1m people.

Colombia's five largest metropolitan areas average 6% annual growth, while the nation's population as a whole gains only 3% annually. Each day 5,000 new arrivals reach São Paulo, attracted by the thriving industries, reports of high wages and better and brighter living conditions. Certainly, whatever they find in the cities can be no worse than what they left behind in the country. Unfortunately, the cities cannot cope with the rush and slums develop to choke every large Latin American city. Lima's slums are growing 10 times faster than the city itself and now have a population of nearly 0·5m. Venezuela, most prosperous of Latin American countries, needs at least 400,000 new cheap urban housing units, as do Chile and Argentina.

Several countries—Chile, Mexico and Bolivia, for example —have ambitious plans to develop vast areas of virgin lands for destitute peasants but so far the results have fallen far short of the plans. In any case, as mechanisation spreads so more and more small farmers or employee farmers are forced out of the countryside. This is one of the costs of progress.

It will be difficult to slow down the rush to the cities and probably impossible to stop it. It is as noticeable in wealthy countries as in the poorer nations. Australia, with 90% of its population south of a line between Adelaide and Brisbane, faces the problem. So do countries so geographically dispersed as the U.S. and Japan, France and India.

New geography must also take into account the remarkable development of the West German and Japanese economies: one could almost refer to the economic empires these two countries are building up. It has for so long been customary to think of the United States as dominating international economy that it would be easy to underestimate the new strength of West Germany and Japan in world trade in all its aspects.* Their importance, one of the major geographic facts of the 1960s, is clear in this book—they are mentioned more than most other countries. Both have vast and complex commercial, industrial, mining, developmental and other commitments.

German influence is widespread, and with good effect for Germany and its economic partners. Experts of various kinds are operating in more than 40 developing nations. In Tanzania, Germany has set up two new agricultural training schools and an agricultural advisory service. In Kenya a large tea-planting project has been implemented with German assistance. In Tunisia experiments are being carried out with German dairy stock. German fishery experts are working as advisors on Africa's west coast. In all, Germany has set up or will set up 63 training schools as part of development aid programmes for South America, Asia and Africa. This is a far greater number than those established by other countries.

East Africa's only establishment for training veterinarians, at Nairobi, Kenya, was equipped by West Germany, and provided with a lecturer and an assistant. A firm from West Germany is to clear 50,000 acres of jungle on the Ivory Coast for new plantations and other Germans will help plant 30,000 acres of land in Cameroon with new oil palm trees. Germany financed and a German company has built a cement factory, capacity 80,000 tons a year, at Loutete in the Congo. These are a few examples of many—and are apart from the scores

* Other countries rapidly increasing in economic importance are Australia, Spain, Israel and Bulgaria, though in different ways and degrees.

of German-owned factories and projects and investments in many countries.*

Similarly, Japan has been systematically arranging contract after contract, all long-term and vast in scope, to keep the country supplied with raw materials for its thriving manufacturing industries. Japan was once known, rather patronisingly, as the "Britain of the East". Now Japan has outstripped its model in many ways—in shipbuilding and steel for example, and in several manufacturing fields.

German and Japanese development has not inhibited other countries. On the contrary, the economy of every country is becoming more and more interlocked and dependent on the economy and prosperity of other countries. Until fairly recently it was the ambition of many a country to be self-sufficient. This impossible ideal—if it *is* an ideal—is now hardly thought of at all. A nation's prosperity depends on good relations, in every sense, with its buyers and suppliers. This is what the Germans and Japanese appear to understand better than anybody else and both now have their imitators.

This integration and inter-nation need is one of the prime facets of modern geography and it is likely to have resounding effects. It can be seen, for instance, in the United States' global commercial "strategy". With as much as half their sales now made outside the U.S., many large corporations have a growing tendency to think and act as global companies with world markets rather than as American companies doing business overseas. Following this trend, Jersey Standard Petroleum has transferred control of European operations to a new subsidiary, Esso Europe, based in London. Esso Europe will oversee a 14-nation area that already sells more oil and petrol than Jersey Standard does in the U.S., and where sales are rising three times as fast. Unlike the old custom of manning overseas offices with a few U.S. executives and a staff of nationals from the nation in which the office is located, Esso Europe is multi-–

---

* Of course, the U.S. continues to support, with money and food, a large part of the world's population. Were it not for American bounty many countries would be in a desperate situation.

national, with an Italian, a Frenchman and a Briton on the board. In microcosm, this shows the general world tendency of co-operation.

The great Dow Chemical company no longer considers itself an American company expanding overseas. In 1966 the company set up Dow Chemical Europe, with headquarters in Zurich. It has two other divisions for Latin America and the Far East. Another large company, Corn Products, has set up a headquarters in Brussels to co-ordinate activities in 14 European countries. Other American companies which have large interests in Europe operate direct from Paris, Amsterdam and Lausanne, among other places.

The U.S. considers Europe the world's most promising "growth market", despite the resistance to the entry of American companies into the Common Market area. Since 1950 Britain has absorbed 4·2 billion dollars in American investment, more than any other country in Europe.* The British particularly want investment that will bring in new technology and foster progress in Scotland and Northern Ireland. Total U.S. investment in Europe (in March 1966) was 12 billion dollars, with Belgium offering perhaps the best outlook, though there have been more new investments in France recently than in any other Common Market country.

Economic union is a widespread and apparently successful phenomenon and the trend towards larger economic units does not seem incompatible with the increase in the number of sovereign states. Of the various reasons in favour of economic union the main one is that many countries are much too small to be viable economic units—Luxembourg, for instance. Elimination of the smaller economic union seems certain considering that only four units—China, India, Russia and the U.S.—contain half of the world's population.

The increasing prosperity of most countries—though, of course, the prosperity can only be relative—together with closer economic links, has the effect of slowly producing a

* Holland is unique in having invested more capital in the U.S. than it has taken from the U.S.

better climate for more lasting peace. The flaw is that current prosperity cannot hope to keep pace with population increase and that after a certain point is reached conditions will deteriorate. India, among other countries, has already reached this point. Where the world goes from there may be more evident by the publication date of the next edition of *New Geography*.

Since much geographical teaching is geared to examinational requirements, it is a pity that examinations so rarely include a question about international bodies such as the Food and Agriculture Organisation, the World Health Organisation, the United Nations Educational, Scientific and Cultural Organisation, the U.N. Technical Assistance Administration, the U.N. Special Fund, the World Bank and several others. These bodies are yet another important facet of modern geography. They cannot find a place in the alphabetical section of this book because they are not new, but their work is progressive and most are mentioned under various countries. In its particular field FAO has achieved great success through its practical, productive and co-operative aims. In March 1966 three more African states, Gambia, Malawi and Zambia, joined the FAO, bringing its total number of members to 114. Basutoland (Lesotho) and Bechuanaland (Botswana) became associate members. A new force in the world, the FAO, from its headquarters in Rome, has a profound though rarely publicised effect on world geography and on its work much of humanity's hope must be pinned.

The FAO realises, for instance, the dramatic changes that can be brought about by using better seed. They rate it so highly that since 1957 they have have had a World Seed Campaign and in 1960 they fostered a World Seed Year. The Organisation's own successes have been illustrative enough. By "selling" Yugoslavia the idea of using Italian wheat, in 1960, the FAO increased the Yugoslav yield by 30 per cent and the country is now wheat self-sufficient. The developed countries are willing enough to share their agricultural discoveries, but the FAO's task of inducing peasant and primitive farmers to adopt them is long, tedious and at times heart-breaking. But the work can be rewarding, too.

When FAO experts first went to Afghanistan in 1958 they found that because of economic and other difficulties power mechanisation was impracticable. The country had a large horse population, so these animals were used to pull light ploughs. The FAO men introduced and had manufactured locally seed drills, light hoes, scythes, threshers and seed cleaners. The result was increased yield of cotton, wheat and sugar beet through improved tillage, better weed control and speedier harvesting. The agricultural economy of the country and the increased mechanical ability of the Afghans has since resulted in the introduction of machines.

The FAO has been the guiding force and in some cases the inspiration behind many other mechanisation projects, for example, in Libya, Morocco, Tunisia, Egypt and Ceylon.

This is typical of the way in which international aid organisations are continually helping to create new geography and why more importance should be given to them in general and scholastic reading.

It is also yet another indication of increasing world co-operation. Such co-operation might not always be inspired by altruistic motives—though altruism is paramount with the FAO. Some other projects are aimed frankly at profits and such an approach is entirely healthy as both parties to a project inevitably benefit. Whatever the motive, the world needs much more co-operation in the 1960s if the great problems facing humanity are to be overcome.

A

ADEN

112,075 sq m. Pop. 1·2m. Aden's fishing industry is developing rapidly and the Protectorate hopes to become an important world fishing centre. Principal centres are in Qu'siti State, with Shihr the most important. The annual catch is approaching 70,000 tons, mainly of sardines, rock-fish, crayfish, tuna, mackerel, mullet and sharks. One-third of the catch is exported, mainly to Ceylon and East Africa, or processed into fish meal and sent to Europe. Already fish accounts for half of Aden's exports. More than 6,000 fishermen are employed with 3,000 boats, many still primitive. The Government's three-year plan, 1965–7, has three main objectives: to survey distribution of fish shoals in the Gulf of Aden; to train fishermen in scientific fishing; to induce investment in new fishery enterprises, e.g. canning. Dhow building, once an important industry in Aden, is now negligible, although old dhows are being refitted and mechanised.

AFGHANISTAN

250,000 sq m. Pop. about 15m (not 12m as often stated). The country is progressing rapidly through U.S. and Russian aid. Soviet engineers have cut the world's highest road tunnel through the Hindu Kush escarpment at Salang Pass. Americans have built a jet airport at Kandahar. Along the Helmand River eight U.S.-financed HEP and irrigation dams are being built. America and Russia are determined to see that Afghanistan remains a buffer state between Russia and India. U.S. aid totalled £150m late in 1966, Russia's aid £250m. There is a flourishing new trade in Persian lamb skins, and oil has been discovered near the Soviet border.

AIR TRANSPORT

The world's fastest growing air-transport market is that between the U.S. and Japan; it has tripled since 1961. Many American companies are competing for the right to operate across the Pacific. Also, many foreign companies now have the right to fly freight and passengers across the United States mainland—a new development.

Japan will allow U.S. airlines to service Osaka, Japan's second largest city, and has dropped its restriction on U.S. all-cargo flights through Tokio. Japan Air Lines are only the third foreign carrier—after BOAC and QANTAS (Australia) —both to fly across the U.S. and to fly all the way around the world. The U.S.'s Trans-World Airlines has no service across the Pacific and Pan American cannot fly across the U.S.

Air transport of goods has undergone great changes in the last two years, so great as to revolutionise the geography of air transport. Half of France's textile exports to the U.S. now travel by air. French perfume manufacturers are now air-freighting perfumes at the rate of 660 tons a year. Greece is sending furs to Germany, Holland and Scandinavia and sea-food to Italy and France—all by air. In 1966 Swissair flew 5m watches to markets abroad, plus great quantities of optical and precision instruments and pharmaceuticals.

The remarkable air-freighting development can be seen by

the 1965 percentage increases in freight for various companies: Air France, Sabena, Scandinavian Airlines System, 20%; Swissair, 22%; BEA, 24%; BOAC, 25%; Pan American, 54%; TWA, 63%.

Air-freighting often costs more than rail or water transport, but can cut manufacturers' distribution bills through cheaper insurance, less pilferage, fewer warehouse and rehandling charges, lighter-weight packaging and faster delivery. One American firm has decided to send all its export goods to Europe by air and expects to save £80,000. Even heavy equipment, traditionally sent by sea, is now moving by air; for example, 10 printing machines from London to Lagos. Despite rapid growth, the percentage of air cargo is, naturally, still small compared with other forms of freighting; trans-Atlantic air-freight accounts for only 1% of the total. But the percentage will rise very rapidly. As a direct result of the new development most air companies have ordered many new transport aircraft. In 1966 Pan American ordered 25 jet freighters at one time.

ALBANIA

10,700 sq m. Pop. 1·8m. Though geographically part of Europe, Albania has succeeded in isolating itself in all ways from both the Western world and from Russia. But progress has always depended on outside help and it is now the Chinese who are helping to build factories and to supply capital equipment and even food. The government plans to make Albania into an industrial nation, an extremely ambitious scheme since the country is so poor and backward.

At Bistrica two HEP plants have been built, largely to exploit the considerable timber reserves and minerals, including iron and bauxite.

ALGERIA

855,000 sq m. Pop. 12·3m. This country is now estimated to have 1% of the world's proven reserves of oil, about 3·6 billion barrels, and 10% of the world's known methane, 79 trillion cubic feet. France has the biggest stake in the reserves and since late 1965 British and U.S. firms have been restricted. In 1966 Algeria made probably £100m in oil taxes. Late in 1965 France promised £175m for a five-year industrialisation programme and is supervising building of petrochemical and steel complexes. France is assured of enough Algerian oil to be virtually independent of Anglo-American oil companies. By paying francs for oil from the only major source within the franc zone France will also save £100m a year in foreign exchange.

Two British methane tankers operate a shuttle service between Algeria and Canvey Island in the Thames Estuary. The pipeline from Laghouat, on the Saharan fringes, to the coast, was built by a British company. It is 500 miles long and cost £25m, and it was opened in 1965.

The new large reservoir of Cheffia across the Wadi Bou Namoussa near Bone (now renamed Annaba) will irrigate 10,000 acres of land and an associated HEP station will aid mineral development.

ALSACE

Booming as never before, partly because of its strategic location near major German population centres. Since Alsatian resurgence began in 1958, 220 new plants have been set up and by the end of 1966 industrial production had risen 55% over that of 1959. Strasbourg is the Central European distribution centre for the South European pipeline from Lavera on the

Mediterranean. Major new works are situated at: Ottmarsheim (chemical plant, Rhône Poulenc); Ile Napoleon (transmission works, Peugeot); Molsheim (aircraft components, Hispano-Suiza); Strasbourg (synthetic rubber, Franco-Canadian Polymer); Colmar (roller-bearings, Timken Roller Bearings, U.S. and Wrigley's Chewing Gum); Huttenheim (electric shavers, Remington Rand); Lauterbourg (ion exchangers, Minoc); Other products are drugs, soups, caffeine-less coffee, clothing.

All this activity has made Strasbourg, 250 miles from salt water, France's biggest port for exports and a major oil refining centre. Alsace, is in effect, the centre of a vast market of 170m customers in the Common Market countries. More than a third of Alsace's new plants are either wholly or partly owned by Germans; the Swiss have 15 plants, the Americans 8.

The new Grand Canal of Alsace, opened in 1965, which runs from Strasbourg to Huningue and then to Basle, is not only a major waterway but provides HEP for the new industries. Some of this power enters the grid system and reaches Britain.

ARGENTINA

1·1m sq m. Pop. 22m. Generally, there was some growth in the economy during 1966 but inflation and consequent devaluations of the peso have undermined confidence among foreign investors. Costs rise steadily. Argentina has been having difficulty in finding markets for primary products, particularly wool and meat. The wheat crops are higher than ever before and large sales were made to new markets—Russia, China and Italy, but 2·3m tons remained unsold from last season. Maize production, 5m tons in 1965, is expected to double by 1969. Rice and cotton production is increasing. But the meat industry, on which Argentina relies so heavily, is passing through critical times. For a long time the main meat-packing stations have been unable to reconcile production costs with prices on the international market and their combined losses in 1965 amounted to £10m.

Nevertheless, Argentine cattle population now numbers 44m and one-sixth of the country is devoted to ranching. More than 180,000 ranchers as well as 788 meat-packing companies and 17% of the nation's labour force (6m) depend on cattle for their livelihood.

Egypt, Israel and Portugal are among Argentina's new markets, and attempts are being made to find markets in Asia and Africa. An Argentine government study estimates that the world market for Argentine beef will reach 820,000 tons by 1970, but I think this is over-optimistic in view of competition from other countries, notably Australia. Also, Argentinians themselves eat 178 lb per head annually—largest consumption in the world—and as the population increases more beef will be needed domestically.

The vast green bulk of the pampas is being cut up into smaller and smaller holdings—a revolutionary development. The land is producing large quantities of wheat and other crops and a £20m irrigation project is transforming the arid pampa south-west of Buenos Aires into a 200,000-acre region that will eventually produce £20m worth of fodder, fruit and vegetables annually.

Industrial activity increased by 7% in 1965 and should repeat this figure in 1966. The iron and steel, cement and coal industries are the most prosperous and motor car production is increasing by about 30% annually. The demands of industry have resulted in increased imports, particularly oil from Venezuela. For instance, the volume of crude oil imported in 1965 was more than 300% greater than the 1964 figure. The 1966 figure is likely to be high. Sales of British-made machinery have fallen off, but capital goods provide the principal opportunities for U.K. manufacturers, and there is scope for the export of non-ferrous metals, iron and steel, chemicals and raw materials. Imperial Chemical Industries has recently built a large group of chemical plants at San Lorenzo, 200 miles from

Buenos Aires. This £10m enterprise is making a vast range of things, from textiles to plastics, and will later transform oil from Argentina's sub-tropical north into polythene and polyester fibre.

The Inter-American Development Bank is financing water and housing projects.

In 1966 work began on the big El Chocon–Los Cerillos dam in Southern Argentina. The £100m project envisages a reservoir 289 sq m. in extent, electricity production of 1·2m kilowatts and irrigation of 1,729,700 acres of land.

The El Cadillal HEP project on the Sali River, just north of Tucumán, was completed in September 1966.

ARMAMENTS

Once again armaments are a big and growing business, especially in Western Europe. The defence budgets of the major NATO powers have increased by about 55% since 1959, but few nations maintain defence establishments large enough to match their ability to produce arms. The result is a fiercely competitive battle for contracts. The arms-makers sell chiefly to their own governments, but most of them vie with one another for NATO contracts and for sales to nations—such as Greece, Portugal and Norway—that do not have their own major armaments industries. Britain does good business in selling arms on the Continent and around the world. West Germany is looking for more export markets. To overcome national bias and to broaden their markets several companies are forming international joint ventures.

ASIA

In a great crescent stretching 10,000 miles from Iran to Japan live more than a quarter of the world's people. This is non-Communist Asia, whose vast size and vaster human reservoir make its bitter struggle for a better life of particular concern to all nations. These are new facts about the area: 80% of the region's export income comes from such primary commodities as rubber, minerals, tea and jute. But commodity prices fluctuate sharply and industrial nations are turning increasingly to man-made substitutes. Asia's foreign exchange reserves are far lower and its trade deficits three times higher than a decade ago. Population growth is increasing five times as fast as food production. The output of food is actually dropping in India, Pakistan, Afghanistan, South Korea, Iran and Nepal. Food output in the area will rise about 5% during the years to 1974 but the U.N. estimates that it must increase about 60% if Asians are to get enough to eat.

The area's manufacturing has been growing at 8% annually, but its share of world industrial output is only 7%, most of which is consumed within the area itself. Inflation is a great handicap: a car costs 44% more in India than in Britain. Japan, Hong Kong and Malaysia have shown how conditions can be improved. A U.N. study group notes that significantly these countries have achieved success without protective measures or other devices that have now come to be accepted as necessary by many countries. Japan, Hong Kong, Formosa, the Philippines and South Korea have all benefited economically from the war in Vietnam, in supplying clothing, food, boots and thousands of items of equipment. (See *Banks*.)

ASTRONOMY

Late in 1965 the Ikeya-Seki comet was discovered by two Japanese observers after whom it was named. It had a 20m-mile tail. It was the fourth and most spectacular comet noted in 1965, adding to a total of about 1700 on record. Ikeya-Seki passed within 300,000 miles of the sun's surface.

It is now known from research at Mount Palomar, California, in 1965, that Jupiter suffers gigantic storms every decade or two. Also, it has been discovered that Jupiter's temperature is minus 225 degrees F, much warmer than the minus 274 degrees F that Jupiter would register if it were an ordinary planet radiating only the heat it received from the sun. The most likely theory is that Jupiter, like a small star, is still contracting under the force of its own gravity.

Chile plans a large group of observatories, which German and Swedish firms will help to build. About 300 miles north of Santiago a research centre with three observatories is being built: it will be able to observe the southern skies after the end of 1967.

The new Australian radio telescope near Canberra can receive the electro-magnetic waves of radio stars up to 10 billion light-years away. The arms of the receiving aerial, which look like windmill sails from the air, are almost a mile long.

Perhaps the most important, and certainly the most spectacular, astronomical discoveries of recent years are those made by Maarten Schmidt at Mount Palomar Observatory. By analysing faint quasar light that travelled billions of years before reaching telescope mirror and camera, Schmidt has uncovered clues to the universe. The remote, starlike objects Schmidt studies were born, and may have died, long before the earth existed. By studying their signals Schmidt has upset the familiar pre-quasar universe of stars and galaxies. His influence has already been profound, for he has undermined established theories and provoked scientists into controversy and hypothesis. The word "quasar" is a corruption of the term "quasi-stellar sources" and has been in use only since 1962. In that year a group of radio astronomers at Parkes, Australia, made definite calculations about the position of the quasar known as 3C 273 ("3C" stands for the Third Cambridge Catalogue of Radio Sources; the other numbers designate each source's position in the sky). Schmidt then calculated, among other things, that 3C 273 is moving away at 15% of the speed of light, or about 28,000 miles a second, and that it was 1·5 billion light-years from the earth. Another astronomer, Greenstein, discovered that quasar 3C 48 was receding even faster than 3C 273 and appeared to be some 4 billion light-years away. In the three years since Schmidt made his first startling calculations noted astronomers have been vying for the distinction of finding the quasar with the largest "red shift"— the wave-length of a quasar's light. The greater the red shift in a galaxy's spectrum the faster the galaxy is speeding away and the farther it is out in space. In January 1966 Schmidt found a quasar with a velocity of 82·2% of the speed of light. So far about 90 quasars have been identified and 30 analysed for red shift, most of them by Schmidt, who believes that eventually about 1000 quasars will be found. The importance of quasars lies in their source. If astronomers can explain their birth they may yet be able to find the secrets of Creation. Other clues have recently been noted. In New Jersey, in February 1966, research workers at Bell Telephone Laboratories recorded what might well prove to be radio waves emitted by a cosmological explosion 10 billion years ago. In February 1966 U.S. Navy scientists reported that an Aerobee rocket had detected strong X-ray sources associated with distant galaxies.

AUSTRALIA

Nearly 3m sq m. Pop. 11·5m. Australia is in the unique position of being the world's most rapidly developing nation. This, of course, is an overall estimate. In some fields it is outpaced by other countries and because of its relatively small population it is necessarily down the scale in other fields. One reason for Australia's recent remarkable development is that it has *room* for development, unlike some other countries which have more nearly reached maximum effort and output. Only an outline can be attempted here in an attempt to bring orthodox textbooks up to date.

Population

Australia has become one of the world's most urbanised nations. One Australian in every two lives in the four largest cities, Sydney, Melbourne, Brisbane and Adelaide. The Australian government is planning for a "balanced population" of 30m, but chances of a more uniform distribution of the extra millions are slight. Population increase is 2% annually.

The old conception of Australia as mainly a primary producing nation, a country of farmers, is quite inaccurate. No less than 35% of the labour force is employed in the 60,000 factories of the manufacturing industries and exports of manufactured goods account for about 15% of Australia's total exports. Over the last decade the annual export of manufactured goods has grown more than twice as fast as Australia's overall exports.

As an example of the general growth of the economy it is only necessary to cite one state, Western Australia, which has had a three-fold increase in economy between 1960 and 1965. It has been described as "the California of Australia", a term which presumably refers to the Mediterranean-climate area in the south-west. In this state 1m acres of land are going into production annually and this figure will continue for several years. Probably the best example of rapid farm development is on the Esperance Plains on Western Australia's south coast, the fastest rural growth area in Ausralia. In less than a decade it has grown from 100 farms to 600 and by 1975 will have 1500 farms.

Despite this success story it is probably true to say that of all the Australian states Queensland is advancing most rapidly with primary industries and New South Wales in secondary industries, though this should not override the general Australian development. In Queensland several million acres of virgin land are being opened to settlement and nine new ports are being built. The mineral resources of Queensland are so vast that their full extent is not yet known. New South Wales contributes nearly half of Australia's secondary industry production, from a total of £2,750m.

Australia is a very large market for Britain and in an average year buys something approaching £250m worth of goods. British ships carry more than a third of Australia's trade. To finance Australian industrialisation more capital has come from Britain than from the rest of the world together. More than 500 leading British companies have direct interests in Australia, which is often described in international financial circles as "the world's best investment area".

Japan has now eclipsed Britain as Australia's main trading partner. Australia takes the Japanese market so seriously that at the 1966 Trade Fair in Osaka it used an exhibition pavilion of 14,000 square feet. Apart from massive quantities of raw materials, Australia is now selling Japan processed foods, wines, textiles, leather goods, jewellery, specialised machinery and equipment, sporting goods and heating appliances. Exports to Japan could easily double in 10 years. In 1966 Japan was taking 30% of Australia's exports, Britain 21%.

Minerals

Iron ore. Some of the world's largest deposits were found in 1964 in north-west Western Australia, notably in the Hamersley Ranges, where capital investment between 1965–70 will reach £167m. Development will necessitate 7 new towns, 5 new ports and 600 miles of railway. During 1967 the first blast furnace of the Broken Hill Proprietory Company in Western Australia will be "blown in" at Kwinana, near Perth. It will produce 600,000 tons of pig iron annually. A £30m iron ore project, being jointly developed by the U.S., Australia and Japan, will be in operation in 1967 on the Savage River in Tasmania. An authoritative survey puts the estimated value of the total production at £350m, although the industry will exploit only a third of the Savage River ore potential. From these and other older fields much more is being exported to Japan. *Bauxite.* On Cape York Peninsula Australia has probably the world's largest deposits of bauxite, much of which is being refined at Gladstone on the Queensland coast and in Tasmania. By mid-1967 the annual output will have reached 2·5m tons, of which about half will be treated at the Gladstone refinery, which will cost £57m when completed. Jarrahdale, Western Australia, is mining so much bauxite that the capacity of the big refinery at Kwinana is being raised from 210,000 metric tons of alumina to 410,000 tons a year. Other vast deposits of bauxite have been located on the Gove Peninsula in the Northern Territory and will soon be developed. Another bauxite mining lease in north-east Arnhem Land, Northern Territory, is held by Pechiney Company of France. *Coal.* The Moura coalfield in central Queensland is being developed to increase production to 4m tons a year, to allow for exports to Japan. *Methane.* Great quantities are now known to exist in southern Queensland; some is already being piped to Brisbane. Two major strikes of natural gas have been made about 15 miles off the Gippsland coast of Victoria. *Gold.* Contrary to general belief, output of gold is not decreasing, but increasing. Main centres now, apart from the old ones of Kalgoorlie and Boulder, are Norseman, Mount Magnet and Mount Ida in Western Australia. *Asbestos.* Wittenoom, Western Australia, is now producing about 13,000 tons. *Lead.* Mine production of lead is the highest in the non-Communist world and Australia's share of the export market in lead concentrates is rapidly increasing. *Copper.* Since December 1965 this has not been exported, but production is high. Over the last decade production of copper has trebled. *Magnesite.* The Broken Hill Proprietory Company, one of the world's largest companies, is to build a plant, probably in South Australia, to produce magnesite from sea water. Dolomite and gypsum are also to be developed in South Australia. A new factory in Tasmania is producing *bitumen* at a rate of 7,500 tons annually. *Ferro-manganese.* At Bell Bay on the Tamar River a new furnace for production of this mineral was completed at the end of 1966. *Zinc.* Four extensions have been made to the plant at Risdon, Tasmania. *Miscellaneous.* It has recently been found that Australia possesses immense quantities of mineral-bearing beach sands containing rutile (titanium dioxide), zircon (used in the jewellery industry, among others) and ilmenite (a mixture of iron, titanium and oxygen).

Farming

Pastoral Farming. Contrary to popular belief, 40% of Australia is suitable for pastoral development and the authoritative figure for the number of sheep in Australia at the end of 1965 was 170m, increasing by 1m a year. (Some textbooks still in use give the figure at 110m.) Cattle numbers are also increasing (see *Beef*). In the Albany region of Western Australia alone the number of beef cattle has increased threefold since 1956. Within a further decade it seems certain that Australia will have millions more beef cattle and considerably more dairy cattle—the latter especially in New South Wales and Victoria—as she acquires new markets. West Germany, Greece, Italy and France are buying increasing amounts of beef. Japan is also now a big buyer of beef, veal, lamb, and mutton. Over the last decade the number of lambs slaughtered in Australian meat works has risen from 8·5m annually to 15·4m.

Fruit. Australia has developed in the last few years as a major world exporter of fruit, both fresh and tinned. Almost every country in Europe and many others are importing Australian fruit, although about 80% (6m cases) of Australia's canned fruit exports are sold in Britain. By new packing and shipping methods Australia has overcome the obvious disadvantage of transport costs over a long distance and is now able to compete with other nations closer to the European market. For instance, Australian oranges are now selling in France.

Arable Crops. Over the past few years there has been renewed expansion in the acreage planted to wheat and in yield per acre. It is generally stated that Australia's yield is about 13·3 bushels per acre; in fact it is now 18·5 bushels owing to improved farming methods. (U.S. yield reaches 21 bushels; Britain, 30 bushels.) Barley, oat and rice production have also greatly increased, but maize production is stagnant.

Sugar. With more than 9,000 plantations, Queensland is now the world's second largest exporter of sugar and within a decade may easily become the largest exporter.

Fishing. Main development has been in cray fishing off the Western Australian coast, where the catch is valued at £4m annually.

Pearling. This industry has declined greatly and only a few boats are now engaged in it. However, cultured pearls, at places near Broome, the traditional pearling centre, have taken over from natural pearls and have become a prosperous industry.

Eggs. Australia now sends to British and Continental markets about 11·5m dozen shell eggs and 10,000 tons of frozen egg.

Transport

Railways. As many other countries close down railways Australia's rail communications are extending, mainly because of the quantity of freight for transport. More than 1,400 miles of new lines are being built or have been approved. During the years to 1971—and perhaps beyond—more railways will be built in Australia than anywhere else in the world.

In 1965 the 603-mile £25m line from the Mount Isa copper mines to Townsville on the Queensland coast was finished. In Western Australia the Avon Valley section of railway, from Midland to Northam, was opened in February 1966. Work is well advanced on 97 miles between Northam and Merredin and 107 miles from Merredin to the iron ore deposits at Kollyanobbing. Completion of this section will enable transportation of large quantities of ore to the steel industry at Kwinana and will take the line to within 125 miles of Kalgoorlie, the final link in the uniform rail gauge across Australia. A great increase in inter-state rail traffic is anticipated on completion of the project.

Motor Cars. Although Australia is already the fourth most motorised country in the world the motor industry is rapidly expanding, with about a 30% annual productivity increase. Currently the figure is 400,000 annually.

Shipping. Australia is developing as a ship-building nation and at Whyalla shipyards (South Australia) three 47,000-ton ore-carriers are under construction. Other freighters are being built in Brisbane and Sydney.

Water. Shortage of water in some areas has always been a handicap, but various schemes are helping to overcome it. Some, such as the Snowy River Scheme, are well known. Newer ones include the Chowilla Dam across the Murray River: when complete it will create a reservoir of more than 500 sq m. and New South Wales, Victoria and South Australia will benefit from it.

Potential

Australia's opportunities are great. It is vigorously seeking new and additional outlets among the developing countries. In efforts to avoid import barriers Australian manufacturers are making capital investments in many Pacific and Asian countries and setting up their own factories in these countries. Trade drives have been sustained around the Mediterranean, in Eastern Europe and even in South America.

AUSTRIA

32,376 sq m. Pop. 7·2m. Austria, like many European countries, is suffering from an acute shortage of labour, despite the increase in the number of foreign workers. The economy suffered a setback in 1965 owing to a severe winter followed by floods. Austria is very dependent on foreign trade and the division of Europe into two trading blocs poses special problems for her. Austria is a member of EFTA and its trade with member countries is increasing. Nevertheless, while EFTA took less than 20% of Austria's products in the first six months of 1966, the EEC, Austria's natural trading partners, took 50%. In spite of increasing tariff discrimination, exports to the EEC are still rising. This is the reason for Austria's wish for some form of association with the Community. Of the Common Market countries, Western Germany heads the list of Austria's markets, accounting for 27·9% of Austria's total exports; then comes Italy with 12·3%. On the balance of payments, Austria shows a surplus, the result of large earnings from tourism. Net income from tourism is increasing by about 15% a year.

Upper Austria is developing increasingly into an industrial area—without damage to the traditional farming and tourist activities. Iron and steel are the most important industries, followed by mining, quarrying, chemical products, glass and pottery.

A recent survey reveals that Austria has approximately 4,700 industrial enterprises, but only about 80 employ more than 1,000 people and the great majority employ less than 100.

The Austrian Danube Power Corporation has a giant scheme for a chain of 13 power dams on the Austrian stretch of the Danube. The new dam at Anschach—the largest river project in Central Europe—is producing one tenth of the country's total electricity output. The river above the station had to be dammed up for a length of 25 miles, which has had the beneficial effect of deepening and widening the river sufficiently for traffic to move in both directions at night without risk. The dam has the largest turbines in Europe outside the Soviet Union and is becoming a tourist attraction.

AUTOMATION

It is slightly beyond the province of this book to delve into the scientific and engineering complexities of automation, but it should be said that industrial experts state that automation has not caused unemployment and that it is not likely to. This was made clear in February 1966 at a meeting in Zurich of the 21 nations of the Organisation for Economic Co-operation and Development. It is clear that automation does not destroy skill or lower the dignity of jobs, but enhances both.

The advance of automation is now most noticeable in West Germany, although it is second to the U.S. in the degree of automation used, followed by Britain and France. By 1970 the U.S. will have 30,000 electronic computers in operation while Europe will have 16,000. Germany will have 4,000 of the European total. This rapid development has profound consequences, particularly in Germany. German business is making thorough use of automation: a third of all electronic computers in Germany are used in industry. In wool-weaving plants, for instance, machines are already performing 12% of the work, in cotton plants as much as 47%. Automation is making the most rapid progress in the mass-production industries—the iron and steel works, petrol refineries, chemical factories and in foodstuffs and tobacco. The Westfalenhutte Steelworks near Dortmund, for example, has one of the most up-to-date, fully automatic and electronically-controlled wide strip rolling mills in the world. An entire major petrochemical plant is controlled from a switchboard watched over by only two people. The control room cost £2·25m, but this is soon recouped. Large central computer centres are scattered throughout the Federal Republic. At these centres many firms have vast calculations worked out. One electronic computer can calculate the wages of 17,000 office workers within half an hour.

Automation will play an ever-increasing part in industrial and economic geography—and, indirectly, in human geography. Also, the machines which provide the automation have created a new and important industry in themselves. U.S. and British computer manufacturers are in constant competition for markets, especially in Europe.

B

BAHRAIN

213 sq m. Pop. 183,000. It has been assumed that Bahrain's oil output would remain static, but in fact production increased by about 9% in 1964, 13% in 1965 and an estimated 18% in 1966. A new offshore field, Abu Sa'fah, shared with Saudi Arabia, was in production in mid-1966 and will further increase production and profits. Bahrain's oil refinery now not only processes its own crude oil, but 8m tons from Saudi Arabia. An economic survey of Bahrain has resulted in several suggestions for diversification and less dependence on oil. Already small industries are in operation to manufacture ice, distilled water, carbon dioxide, cement blocks, woollen clothing. The Bahrain entrepôt trade has tended to decline in recent years. The modern settlement of Isa, about four miles from the capital, Manama, will accommodate 40,000 people by 1968.

BANKS

The Asian Development Bank was launched in Manila at the end of 1965 following a 26-nation meeting. The bank is Asia's first common venture and one of the very few joint ventures of any kind brought to fruition in Asia's history. The bank, a regional version of the World Bank, will fight Asia's crushing poverty by financing industry, power, roads and transport. Asian governments supplied £225m of the initial capital and the U.S. £67m. The bank will make loans for a maximum period of 25 years at $5\frac{1}{2}\%$ interest. The bank is an idea unique among efforts to aid the world's poor and is taking shape at a time when development aid to the world's poor countries is falling steadily behind their needs. Despite rising prosperity in the U.S. and Europe, the flow of aid from these sources has remained static at £3 billion a year, which amounts to 0·9% of the developed nations total output of goods and services. The bank will be followed by similar institutions for Latin America and Africa.

BARBADOS

166 sq m. Pop. 275,000. This island is undergoing rapid changes. The deep water harbour has berths for 8 ocean-going ships, storage for 80,000 tons of sugar, which is half the annual production, and transit sheds for storing imports. Sugar can now be loaded five times as fast as when ships had to load from lighters. Income from tourism is increasing by about £4m a year. Barbados became independent on November 30th, 1966.

BASUTOLAND (now LESOTHO)

11,716 sq m. Pop. 880,000. This enclave needs a massive infusion of foreign investment, especially for success of the projected Ox-bow HEP scheme. Britain had doubled financial aid to £2m. The Colonial Development and Welfare Fund gives £1m annually. With the coming of independence there are plans for a great dam on Ox-bow Lake, to provide power for industries which may help to keep at home some of the 180,000 men who work in the gold and diamond mines of South Africa.

BAUXITE

It is difficult to keep abreast of the rapid development in bauxite mining. Reference will be found under various country headings. Also, rich deposits have been found north of Lake Balaton, Hungary, and in the middle of the Kyzyl-Kum desert, Uzbekistan. In the Italian province of Lecce new quarries are producing 500 tons a day. Production began at the Kobé mines, Guinea, late in 1965. In Costa Rica the large firm ALCOA is to develop mines around San Isidro del General. In French Guiana very large deposits at Kaw Mountain are expected to yield 700,000 tons annually. In nearby Suriname bauxite is now not only mined but smelted—at Brokopondo.

(See especially *Australia* and *Jamaica*.)

BECHUANALAND (now BOTSWANA)

222,000 sq m. Pop. 0·5m. A succession of drought years has devastated this country. In the east the harvest has been an almost total failure and more than 50% of the cattle have died. Late in 1966 Bechuanaland became the Republic of Botswana and fully independent of Britain.

The Freedom From Hunger Campaign is hoping that, within the next five years, farmers will be able to grow six bags of grain an acre instead of two and that water will be available for cattle, through the building of many small dams—about thirty a year. At the time of independence Britain gave Botswana £16m for famine relief and economic development. The country sells its goats, cattle and hides to South Africa and 40,000 of its men have jobs in the gold mines and factories of Johannesburg.

BEEF

The United States has supplanted Britain as the largest importer of Australian beef: she imports great quantities for her hamburger trade. Australia has built new meatworks at Darwin and Katherine in the Northern Territory for this expanding industry; she now has 16,500,000 beef cattle, mostly Red Polls, Herefords and Shorthorns.

The U.S. imports £100m worth of beef a year, most of it cooked or canned because of rigid laws prohibiting imports of fresh or fresh-frozen beef that might contain virus of foot and mouth disease. Most imported beef goes into hot dogs or canned stews, or is brought in as canned corned beef. The U.S. has now agreed to accept frozen cooked beef, but only from packers who meet U.S. Agriculture Department standards. (See *Argentina*.)

BELGIUM

11,870 sq m. Pop. 9·8m. Belgium remains an important market for U.K. products, but progressive removal of tariff barriers within the Common Market is making competition more intense. Textile production, which began to fall in 1964, has fallen still further, partly owing to competition from low-priced imports (India, Hong Kong). Labour shortage is a great problem and workers are being brought from as far afield as Greece and Turkey. Exports are increasing, as are imports from Britain. British manufacturers are finding a promising market for high quality foods, household goods, medical and dental instruments and building materials. However, Belgium's main trading partners are Holland and Western Germany. General Motors Corporation, America, has begun to build a huge automative assembly plant near Antwerp. It will cost an estimated £36m and will assemble Opel, Reckard and Kadett cars. The plant will employ about 6,000 people. The Belgian government is trying to induce other foreign companies to build factories.

In the last 15 years coal production has fallen by a third and continues to fall. Six more mines closed during 1966. However, steel production is at a high level—9m tons in 1965. Petroleum refining is probably Belgium's most successful industry, with an increase of 16% in 1965. Do not be misled by this high figure: Belgium's general growth rate is the lowest of the Common Market countries.

Much of Belgium's development hinges on Antwerp which is not only developing its port facilities but is rapidly becoming a petrochemical centre of world importance. From the reports of bankers and industrialists Antwerp is Europe's fastest-growing industrial hub.

BOLIVIA

415,000 sq m. Pop. 3·7m. Bolivia's income per head has *risen*
to £43. (U.K. £489.) The economy, as is well known, is founded
on tin. The nation's present contribution to the world total is
16%. Although tin dominates the export market—90% of it—
for the first time tungsten, lead, zinc and silver have much
better prospects. A rich deposit of iron ore has been found in
the south-east, but has received little publicity. Also, recent exploration has revealed vast gold reserves, estimated to be as
much as £1,070m, in an area which could be producing £8m
annually by 1972. A West German company is mining zinc and
helping to modernise the tin industry. In addition, some progress has been made in the oil and methane industry.

A 10-year plan, 1963–73, for social and economic development has been revised, with three main objectives: to promote
the mining and petroleum industries; to create local industries
so as to reduce imports; to develop farming. The Inter-American Development Bank and the World Bank have lent money.
Britain is a major importer of Bolivian products, but there is
little reciprocal trade except, very recently, in mining equipment. The basic government plan is to take people away from
the *altiplano* and resettle them on farms near Santa Cruz,
Cochabamba and Caranavi; about 50,000 people a year are
moving. By 1971 the government hopes to spend £40m on new
roads to facilitate resettlement.

BRAZIL

3·3m sq m. Pop. 82·5m (not 66·3m as given in a recent encyclopaedia). The country's economy has been changing rapidly.
The development programme, in force until the end of 1966,
was principally designed to stabilise the economy, which

suffered from inflation. The cost of living in 1964 was running at a rate of 140%, but has been cut back. Many companies producing cars, steel, textiles and consumer goods have gone bankrupt. Agriculture still provides a living for more than half the working population and farm products account for the major proportion of export earnings. Output of coffee, the main crop, was affected by severe drought and frost in 1964 and in 1965 the total production amounted to 32m bags— 43% of the world total. Brazil's export quota, under agreement with the International Coffee Council, in 1966 amounted to 17·5m bags, about 37% of the world market.

Despite difficulties, the outlook for Brazil is more hopeful than it has been for several years. In the long-term the country has enormous potential wealth, but its exploitation depends on political stability. These are some new facts about Brazil:

It has the world's greatest HEP potential. Much depends on the HEP station on the Tres Marías barrage.

With 16% of the world's forests, Brazil exports £32m worth of pine a year and will, by 1970, produce all its own pulp and paper.

Plans are being made to exploit the 1,800 kinds of edible fish in Brazilian waters.

Bauxite and iron mining are to be developed. The country has an estimated 65 billion tons of iron ore. In 1967 a steel works will be completed in the Bahia hinterland and will produce 130,000 tons of sheet steel annually. Brazil announced recently that it hopes to increase its present steel production figure of 4·5m tons to 10m tons annually by 1970. In 1957 about 40% of vehicle motors and spare parts were produced in Brazil; in 1960 the figure was more than 90% and in 1966 it was 99%.

The latest mineral find is that of white crystal. Scene of the find is Cristalina, 60 miles south of Brasilia. The deposit is said to be "virtually limitless".

Most important, at the town of Serra do Navio in the Amapa region of the Amazon Basin the ICOMI organisation

(Industria e Comercio de Minerios) is exploiting one of the world's largest known reserves of manganese. Owned 51% by Brazilians and 49% by Bethlehem Steel Corporation (U.S.), ICOMI has brought other industries to Brazil. A Swedish company has built a ball-bearing plant near São Paulo. ICOMI has laid a 122-mile railway through the jungle, dredged a stretch of the Amazon to handle ocean-going ships and has built docks and roads.

The pacemaker of progress in Brazil is the state and city of São Paulo, which now has a population of 4·4m. More than half of Brazil's production is concentrated in São Paulo State, with its population of 12m. By the middle of 1966 São Paulo city had 66,000 industrial enterprises (Chamber of Commerce figure). The state is the home of 91% of the nation's automobile output; 75% of its aluminium; 70% of its iron and iron alloy production and 80% of its synthetics.

In the central plateau great developments are being made. Apart from many vegetable crops, the central state of Goiás now has 4,000,000 cattle. Settlements are sprouting along the road between Brasilia and Belém. In 1958 Araguaiana was a road-construction camp. It now has a population of 8,500 people and in late 1966 had a large factory refining oil from native babacu nuts, peanuts, cotton and sunflower seeds. It will manufacture the cans for the oil and the mahogany cases for the tins. Belém, at the northern terminus of the road, is no longer a struggling river port, but a thriving commercial centre of 450,000 people. It ships rubber, jute and pepper to the south. Cidade Presidente Kennedy, founded in April 1964, had a population of 1,500 in mid-1966. Many minerals—nickel, tin, lead, zinc, copper, gold, diamonds and quartz—will provide the central plateau with further prosperity.

Much of the credit for Brazil's recovery is due to the Minister of Economic Planning, Roberto de Oliveira Campos. Among other steps, he eliminated £70m in government subsidies on wheat, oil and newsprint.

Foreign investors are responding. Alcoa plans an £18m aluminium project. Volkswagen will double its production of cars to 120,000 annually and American Ford is building a £10m plant. The U.S. and the World Bank are also once again investing in Brazil.

BRIDGES

Few people realise that bridge-building is now one of the world's big industries and that communications are more than ever geared and located in conjunction with new bridges. Since 1959 Britain has built 140 bridges as parts of new highways and by the 1970s will have built 280 more. Germany builds 1,000 new bridges a year and during 1966 had under construction nine spans more than 3,000 feet long. Since 1959 the U.S. has spent 7 billion dollars on 20,000 new bridges (the country has 500,000 bridges) and before 1974 will spend another 10 billion dollars. Nearly all the steel bridges used in Germany today incorporate a German-developed steel plate called orthotropic. On a conventional bridge the concrete roadway is supported on steel stringers. An orthotropic bridge, instead of a concrete slab, has a half-as-heavy steel deck serving both as roadway and stress-carrying component of the bridge spans.

An American company, United States Steel International, is building the Tagus River Bridge. It will have the longest span in Europe and is the longest bridge in the world designed for both highway and rail traffic. The same company recently began work on the Orinoco River Bridge, South America's longest.

Asia's longest road bridge—two miles long—has been completed over the Sone River in the province of Bihar. It cuts the distance between Calcutta and New Delhi by 125 miles.

BRITAIN

93,053 sq m. Pop. 54m. It is often said that the United Kingdom's position in the world is declining, but this is not only mis-
leading but inaccurate. Britain remains one of the great
industrial, trading and shipping nations and her economy has
been improving. It is not possible here to deal with every aspect
of British economic geography, but the main current developments are mentioned.

Shipping. Despite the successes of foreign competitors Britain
is still important and often has more orders in hand than most
other countries. (See *Ships & Shipping.*) Rolls Royce engines
power half the free world's air fleets; half the world's shipping
fleet has British navigational equipment.

Diet. As an indication of prosperity, British people consume
more calories per head than any of the Common Market
countries and their diet is better. The British are a close second
to the French in meat consumption, but they eat more
fish, eggs, butter and milk than the Common Market
countries. Danish bacon holds 48% of the British bacon
market, but British bacon has been increasing in quantity
and quality.

Ports. The greatest threats to British exports are strikes and
crowded, inefficient ports. Until ports are expanded and
modernised much trade will be diverted to Rotterdam and
Antwerp. One step towards meeting Continental competition is
the idea of a third major port, to take the strain off London
and Liverpool. Portbury on the Bristol Channel will probably
be the site. The Port of Bristol Authority had already
planned a £27m extension at Portbury, to link with Bristol
docks. The National Ports Council sees the Portbury development as only the first stage in building a vast system of docks
on both sides of the Bristol Channel. Portbury was chosen in
preference to Southampton and South Wales partly because of
the excellent motorway connections which will become available with London, the Midlands and South Wales. The site

makes it possible to build a port on the most modern lines, and this is essential to attract shipping. Immingham on the Humber is to be developed to provide the biggest bulk handling port in Western Europe by 1968.

Resources and Products. Britain's crops have all reached record levels in the last few years and some industries have been remarkably prosperous, e.g. motor vehicles; petrochemicals; aluminium smelting (because of increased HEP at such places as Kinlochleven); equipment for factories and even entire factories; publishing—Britain is the world's largest supplier of books. Livestock numbers have greatly increased, especially poultry. (See *Coal*.)

Imports, Exports, Trade. For 1965 exports rose by 7%, a rate well above average. The increase occurred mainly in the U.S. market, where British sales were 23% higher than in 1964. Exports of transport equipment, especially ships and aircraft, showed a sharp advance.

Imports in 1965 averaged £480m a month, only one per cent more than in 1964. The average overseas trade deficit during the year was halved from £45m monthly to £23m. British trade has grown with many countries. Israel is an example. In 1960 British exports to Israel amounted to £21·4m. In 1965 they amounted to £60m.

Until 1975 at least there will be an export market in hospitals and Britain should do well in this market, largely through the British Hospitals Export Council, formed in April 1964. The quality and price of British equipment is competitive even with German and Swiss equipment, but delays in delivery and the inadequacy of after-sales service may damage British prospects.

Farm machinery accounts for more than 4% of Britain's total revenue from exports. Only four manufacturing industries export more—the motor vehicle industry, the chemical industry, the electrical machinery industry, and the iron and steel. British farm machinery goes to more than 160 individual territories.

British tractors are finding many markets in Europe. The

Ford Company has filled or is filling very rich orders from 13 countries, including £3m worth of tractors from Finland and £2·5m to Denmark. During 1966 Ford expected to increase tractor exports by a further 25%. The company has a plant at Antwerp where, in 1966, it expected to assemble and sell tractors worth £14·6m. Other large buyers of British tractors are Australia, South Africa, Mexico, New Zealand, Venezuela and Chile.

Nuclear Power. Britain is the world's leading nuclear power nation and has produced more nuclear electricity than the rest of the world together. Britain has two stages in plan. In the first all the stations are "Magnox" stations, a name derived from the fuel elements—rods of natural uranium—being cased in magnesium alloy. The reactors use graphite to slow down the action of the reactor and pressured carbon dioxide is blown through the reactor core to remove heat. The gas is then passed through a heat exchanger where water is heated into steam to drive the generators. So far nuclear power is dearer to produce than coal-fired or oil-fired electricity—despite the lower running costs in nuclear stations—but with experience and improved techniques there is reason to hope that it will eventually be competitive in price. Britain has or will have commercial nuclear stations at Hunterston (Argyll) 1964; Wylfa (Anglesey) in 1968–9; Trawsfynydd (Merionethshire) 1965; Berkeley (Gloucester) 1962; Oldbury (Gloucester) 1966; Hinckley Point (Somerset) 1965; Sizewell (Suffolk) 1965; Bradwell (Essex) 1962; Dungeness (Kent) 1965 where a second station will be in operation in 1970. The third fuel, as nuclear generation is called, has many attractions, not the least being that the power stations should be largely independent of foreign supplies, unlike those dependent on oil. Competition is likely to be strong, especially in the large potential market for design and supply of nuclear power stations abroad. Britain should be able to hold the lead, with 10% of her electricity requirements already being produced by nuclear power.

Methane (Natural Gas). Finds of natural gas in Yorkshire and in the North Sea are tremendously important to Britain.

The Shell-Esso North Sea strike alone is said (May 1966) to be able to produce 2,000m cubic feet of gas a day: this is twice the current output of the entire British gas industry. And this is small when compared with the first estimate by British Petroleum (in which the British government has a $51\frac{1}{2}$% interest) when it discovered gas in the North Sea—10m cubic feet a day: this has since been raised to a minimum of 50m. In June 1966 Phillips Petroleum announced a strike with a flow of 17m cubic feet a day.

The strike in Yorkshire, at Lockton near Scarborough, is potentially even more important. Drilling from this first substantial find on land in Britain has produced between 5m and 10m cubic feet a day. In size it approaches that made by the rig *Sea Gem*, which collapsed and sank in the North Sea in December 1965, after a find said to be capable of producing 10m cubic feet a day. Because of the considerably lower cost of drilling on land it seems that Yorkshire gas, when exploited, will be available to the Gas Council at a lower price than North Sea supplies.

Oil Refineries. New refineries, to be complete in 1967 or 1968: Teesport, between Redcar and Middlesbrough; Killingholme, on the Humber near Immingham; Isle of Man between Rue Point and Point of Ayre; Canvey Island.

Development in the North-East. Of all British regions the North-East has changed most radically. In 1964 it was suffering from depression and unemployment: now it is thriving. Government encouragement to industry has brought many new firms—130 in 1965 alone, bringing the total number of companies to about 3,500. Shipbuilding and coal still play a dominant part in employment, accounting for 17% of the working population, but this dominance is decreasing. Between mid-1966 and mid-1968 pit closures will make 25,000 workers redundant, but new firms will create about 40,000 jobs. Imperial Chemical Industries is the largest employer, with 36,000 workers.

Scotland. In June 1966 Scotland had 58,450 unemployed, but at the same time at least 55,000 jobs were on the way in a new drive for prosperity. Massive development by the U.S. (Caterpillar Tractor, National Cash Register, and IBM for example), by Italy (Olivetti), and England (BMC, Rootes, Ferranti, Elliott Automation) has given Scotland the balanced economy it needed. Before the seamen's strike of May 1966 Scotland expected to export goods worth £400m—10% more than in 1965.

Generally the main handicaps to Britain's remaining a competitively industrial nation are poor labour-management relations, strikes and restrictive practices and labour shortages.

BULGARIA

43,000 sq m. Pop. 8·2m. The entire economic geography of Bulgaria has changed. The country, once almost wholly agricultural, is now so industrialised that half the national income is produced by manufactures. In 1946 more than 70% of the people lived on farms: in 1966 only 47% lived there. All targets have been exceeded in a remarkable story of success. The metallurgy, rubber, chemical and machinery industries have been specially profitable. Bulgaria is now a major producer of lead, zinc and copper; the world's largest exporter of tomatoes (approaching 250,000 tons annually); a major exporter of fresh fruit, vegetables, tobacco and cigarettes.

Other exports include jams, jellies, butter and milk, as well as batteries, machine tools, pumps, electric hoists, pharmaceuticals and steel products.

About 80% of the country's trade is with Communist countries, especially Russia, with which Bulgaria has a five-year trade agreement, 1966–70. Tourism as an industry has expanded greatly with more than 1m tourists in 1966 and 1¼m expected in 1967, most of whom are attracted by the Black Sea resorts. As an adjunct to the growing tourist industry, the U.S. Coca-Cola Company is building a large bottling plant at

Varna, on the Black Sea coast. Britain has a five-year trade agreement with Bulgaria and will probably sell much large machinery.

BURMA

262,000 sq m. Pop. 24m. The one part of the Burmese economy not nationalised is farming, and so it is no coincidence that farming is the only industry still successful. However, even this must be qualified, for it is only rice that is in abundance: the yield in 1965 was 7·5m tons, providing plenty for export. Onions, chili peppers, salt and cooking oil—essentials in Burmese diet—are rigidly rationed. Regrettably, most of Burma's new geography is negative: even teak, a traditional export, has declined in importance, from 200,000 tons exported in 1939 to 80,000 in 1965. The government has publicised improvements in communications, but little has been achieved. According to a survey in 1965 only 12½% of the country's area is cultivated, but the government hopes to raise this figure to 20%. Forest and woodland still cover 57%. Under the government's development plan of 1962 a steel rolling mill, a jute bag and twine mill, two cotton spinning and weaving mills, a pharmaceutical plant, a large HEP plant and three sugar factories have been built, but reports indicate disappointing production figures. A loan of £30m from Communist China in 1963 helped to finance these projects.

C

CAMBODIA

70,000 sq m. Pop. 5·8m. Cotton has been declining for some years and has now almost disappeared. Maize, too, has declined sharply since 1963, while tobacco, kapok and sesame have increased in yield. Cultivation of rubber is increasing rapidly. Grown scientifically, as a plantation crop, it gives a yield of 1 ton per acre, the highest in the world. Rice—1·35m tons in 1965—remains the dominant crop. Industry remains unimportant, but it is developing. By the end of the current Five-Year Plan (1963–7) a tyre factory, iron and steel works, a jute mill and a general engineering factory—all in Phnom Penh—will have been added to the light industries already set up. French financial interest in Cambodia is paramount and amounts to £20m, chiefly in the rubber plantations that provide jobs for 20,000 and bring in £5m annually in foreign currency.

CANADA

3·9m sq m. Pop. 19·705m. Canada is buying an increasing quantity of food from Australia, mainly beef, lamb, mutton, sugar, raisins and other fruit. Total value £A22m. Australia buys only £A1·3m worth of food from Canada.

Canada's sales of wheat to the Soviet Union and China have

greatly increased prosperity. The gross national product is expanding at 6% annually: exports have risen 8%. In August 1965 Canada announced the sale of 187m bushels of wheat to Russia, an order second only in history to Russia's purchase of 239m bushels in 1963. The sale raised Russia's total 1965 order for Canadian wheat to 222 billion bushels, all of which was delivered by August 1966. Coupled with other sales to Communist China, Czechoslovakia and Bulgaria, the sale to Russia accounted for Canada's entire 1965 crop. Similar deals are very likely for the next few years, unless Russian agriculture improves and is not damaged by too much or too little rain.

The large HEP plant at Twin Falls on Unknown River, near Churchill Grand Falls, Labrador, commenced operations late in 1966, supplying power for the iron ore and timber industries.

In October 1966 U.S. firms owned 1,500 major companies; controlled 46% of the country's manufacturing; 52% of its mining and smelting and 62% of its petroleum and gas industries. The U.S.'s biggest customer, Canada buys 25% of American exports and sells the U.S. 70% of its own exports.

CANALS

Volga-Baltic Canal. Although its shores touch two oceans and 12 seas, the Soviet Union is practically a landlocked nation. It has too few ports and those are often on icebound waters and too far from major population centres. The Soviet Union believes that the Volga-Baltic canal, opened in May 1965, but still being developed, will revitalise shipping and trade. A ship can load in the Iranian port of Nowshahr and travel 4,300 miles to Hamburg. The new canal cuts the average shipping time from Iran to Germany from 50 to 25 days and cuts 2,700 miles from the circuitous route. The heart of the waterway is a 224-mile stretch in Western Russia, where 39 old locks were replaced by seven modern ones. Icebreakers are keeping the route open in winter. Moscow is linked to the canal by a new spur canal and recent publicity calls Moscow the "Port of the Five Seas", because it is now linked with the Baltic, Black, White, Azov and Caspian Seas.

Rhine-Main-Danube Canal. This canal, at present being widened and deepened to take ships of 1500 tons for 423 miles, will link the Western European network of waterways with the Danube and thus establish a continuous shipping route from the North Sea to the Black Sea. This means that in 1967 a new route, 2,125 miles long, will exist between the ports of Holland, Belgium, France, Switzerland and Western Germany and the trading centres of Austria, Yugoslavia, Hungary, Czechoslovakia, Bulgaria, Rumania and the Soviet Union. The importance for Europe's overall economy cannot be forecast accurately, but the turnover of goods on the River Main has tripled in the past few years. The canal's maximum capacity is calculated at 55m tons. (The Panama Canal's maximum capacity is 75m tons.) Branch canals will join the main canal to such industrial centres as Ulm and Augsburg. Several power stations are being built on the main canal and rivers.

Moselle Waterway. Metz and Coblenz are linked by this easily navigable waterway and with the widening of the river between Metz and Frouard, completed in 1966, the city of Nancy is virtually linked with the Rhine. French steel now takes the cheapest if not the quickest route to Germany and for export overseas from Rotterdam: Ruhr coal now traverses the Moselle to the heart of the French iron and steel industry. The canal is only part of a larger scheme for improving and developing France's natural river network and its strategic canals.

Rhine-Rhône. French plans for the Rhine-Rhône canals will revolutionise the industrial patterns of Europe, for even large vessels will be able to avoid the long sea haul through the Straits of Gibraltar, the Bay of Biscay and the English Channel.

Much work has already been done and the only difficult stretch is that which will link the Saone, which flows south from the Vosges, to the Moselle. It is due for completion in 1970.

Rouen-Northern France. Another ambitious canal project will link Rouen, where the Seine ceases to be tidal, with the northern coalfields. Canalisation of the Seine has long allowed Paris to feed its heavy industries through Rouen, but the new waterway will connect the north by water to Paris and to the Channel. The same industrial region will ultimately have another canal outlet to the English Channel through Dunkirk.

Panama Canal. As the Panama Canal (51 miles) will be obsolete in A.D. 2000 and inadequate long before that, plans are being made for a new canal through the Isthmus of Panama. The canal is handling too much traffic to be efficient. About 50% of Japan's exports to the West pass through it. Equador, Peru and Chile depend on it for between 75% and 90% of their total imports and exports. The biggest tankers cannot use the Canal.

The three most likely routes for the new canal are: (1) The San Blas route, 40 miles long, which runs through well populated territory. (2) Sasardi-Morti Route, 60 miles. (3) Atrato-Truando Route, 100 miles, in Colombia.

The cost of blasting a new canal with atomic explosives would be only a quarter that of excavating by conventional techniques. Using conventional methods a canal would cost £825m and take 10 years: with atomic explosions a new canal could be produced in six years at a cost of £210m.

Sacramento Riverway. Strictly speaking, the Sacramento River deep-water ship channel is not new, for the first ship used it in July 1963, but it has received practically no publicity. The channel, which is 43 miles long and 30 feet deep, means that Sacramento, which had for long been a trading backwater, is now the major outlet for about 1½ billion dollars worth of agricultural products annually from California, Oregon and Nevada. Sacramento's new port facilities include several huge grain silos (elevators), berths for many ships and 4,500 feet of automated dock space. Sacramento is intent on becoming more than a big port. Oil refineries and chemical plants have already been attracted to the banks of the river and it seems likely that before long Sacramento port will be expanded: five miles of deep-sea berths could be provided if necessary.

CENTRAL AMERICA

The Central American Common Market, consisting of Guatemala, El Salvador, Honduras, Nicaragua and Costa Rica is one of the fastest growing areas in Latin America. Economic expansion continued in each country throughout 1966. Virtually all external customs duties had been made uniform and agreement on the remainder was reached during 1966. A common customs administration will be adopted by 1970. By September 1965 95% of internal duties had been abolished: the remainder, removed by the middle of 1966, covered such things as dairy products, coffee, petroleum and petroleum products, all controversial because individual countries have vested interests. Development in Central America is dependent on foreign investment. One of the aims of the Central American Common Market is to establish a full monetary union. Trade among the five countries was valued at only £18m in 1962: the estimated figure for 1966 was £40m.
(See individual countries.)

CEYLON

25,332 sq m. Pop. 10·9m. An "Aid to Ceylon" consortium has been established, the member countries being Australia, Canada, Japan, Britain, the U.S., Germany and India, with help from the World Bank. Ceylon has needed help urgently, for the economy has been weak. Production of tea, the mainstay of the economy, has fallen. Britain is Ceylon's largest supplier and largest buyer, but sales and purchases have fallen off. Britain takes 35% of Ceylon's tea, but there has been a continuing decline in British consumption in recent years.

About 90,000 acres of plantations have been replanted with rubber under a five-year programme to be completed in 1967, but synthetic rubber is causing serious competition.

Ceylon is too dependent on tea and rubber, and so industrialisation is being encouraged, especially in textiles, salt and cement. The Gal Oya irrigation scheme is successful, but other projects are necessary if Ceylon's economy is to keep pace with the 3% population increase.

CHILE

300,000 sq m. Pop. 8·6m. Chile faces pressing problems, the most serious being inflation. In 1964 the rise in cost of living was 38%; in 1965, 25%. The government hoped to hold the increase to 15% for 1966 and 10% for 1967. The government is confident, too, that production of copper, at present 600,000 metric tons annually, can be doubled by 1970. Refining capacity is to be so stepped up that Chile will be the world's third largest refiner.

Many major development projects are to be financed wholly or partly by foreign capital—100 by West Germany alone. On average, Chile has been receiving £64m annually in foreign assistance in recent years and in 1965 the U.S. government supplied £45m for economic development.

Agriculture is increasing at a rate of only 2%, while the population is growing by 3%. £30m annually is spent on import of basic foods. Agrarian reform recently announced calls for the compulsory sale of large unproductive estates and for the creation of 100,000 new smallholdings. Irrigation is to be extended. Chile's fishing industry is developing and it has ambitions plans to export more timber to Europe from southern Chile. The U.K. exports goods worth £11m to Chile and imports commodities worth £30m each year.

One of the German-financed projects is the new settlement of Poblacion Berlin, a satellite town of Valparaiso. Another interesting Chilean project concerns the Lauca River towards the Bolivian border. The Chileans have reversed part of the eastward-flowing Lauca as a power project to supply future demands of industry, railway and urban development in the department of Arica. At one point the water has been diverted into a concrete-lined canal which carries it 20 miles across the high Chilean Puna to a point above Chapiquina, where a power house was completed in 1965. The total effective fall of this system is nearly 4,000 feet, entirely within the mountain. The whole system is bound up with the government's plan to make Arica a major port, industrial and marketing centre. (See *Irrigation*.)

CHINA

4·3m sq m. Pop. 750m approximately. 1965 was a period of consolidation for the Republic, with slow but steady recovery from mismanagement and natural disasters. Lack of official statistics makes an accurate picture difficult to obtain, but it is true that better harvests have brought improvements. A third Five-Year

Plan began in January 1966, with emphasis on agriculture and expansion of light industry. Priority is being given to the development of electricity supplies and to the production of fertilisers for agriculture. Attention will also be given to chemicals, steel and machinery. No accurate figures are available, but reports indicate that industrial production increased by 12% in 1965, the main gains being in fertilisers, crude oil, machine tools, motor vehicles, cement, plastics and chemical fibres. China has bought lorries worth £10m from France and diesel locomotives from West Germany. China claims it is self-sufficient in oil. As its oil consumption is among the lowest in the world, this could be so.

It seems possible that the sugar, soyabean, peanut, cotton and oilseed crops have increased by 15% to 40% over the 1964 figures. If plans for agricultural output have been successful, then food supplies are keeping just ahead of the population growth of $2\frac{1}{2}$%. China is importing fertiliser from Japan and from Europe.

Wheat and other grains have improved in quality and yield, but China has an annual purchase commitment with Canada until the end of 1969 at least. It will continue to buy wheat from Australia and, now, from Argentina. Hong Kong is becoming even more of a major outlet for China's exports—agricultural products, textiles and cheap consumer goods. British exports to China have grown from £9m in 1962 to £25m in 1965 and an estimated £30m in 1966. Imports from China amounted to £28m in 1965. Chinese industrialists have been visiting Britain. They are interested in buying complete plants of many different kinds and a £30m power station is a possible sale. China's prospects are better than at any time since 1945. At a trade fair in Canton, China exhibited lathes, printing presses and weaving looms. Japan is probably China's biggest market, while France could well become one of China's biggest suppliers.

It is interesting to note that each year China is now making £2m from the sale of human hair for the foreign wig market. Quite 95% of China's poultry and 80% of the pigs are now privately produced and sold in small free markets in the villages. The government was forced to allow this free enterprise in an effort to enliven the economy. Between 1966 and 1970 China will have spent £5 billion annually in building plants and factories of various kinds.

The government has announced that parents who have more than three children will, in future, be severely penalised. The punishments are so strict that the defaulters would starve to death. (See *Population*.)

COAL

As a commodity, coal has been declining under the impact of oil, methane, HEP and commercial nuclear power. In many countries it can only decline still further, as it has virtually no advantages, as a source of power, over the newer forms of power supply. What has been happening to coal in Britain may be taken as an example of what is happening elsewhere, notably in Belgium, Western Germany and Italy.

Britain's National Coal Board is the third largest industrial company outside the U.S. and employs 550,000 people—one in every 40 workers. It suffers from a large deficit, is closing many mines and late in 1965 it announced plans to dismiss 14,000 clerical employees. Like coal industries everywhere, the NCB suffers from the increased efficiency of oil, natural gas and nuclear power. In 1950 coal supplied 90% of Britain's fuel needs: in 1966 the figure was only 62%. Coal production costs have risen steadily, partly because of the absenteeism of 25,000 men daily. Protective measures such as a virtual ban on coal imports, and a 2d-a-gallon tax on oil, have been ineffective. About 120,000 miners will lose their jobs as a result of pit closures. The coal yield for 1966 was between 180 and 200 million tons. The peak figure was 237m tons in 1937 and in

1950 it was 220m. The point is that while overall consumption of fuels increases, coal's share declines.

Despite the poor future for coal, between 1958 and 1959 the NCB prospected for coal under the North Sea. Eighteen bore-holes, averaging 2,000 feet deep, were drilled from a sea-boring tower specially built for the purpose. The operations proved that at least 550m tons of coal that could be worked from existing collieries lie beneath the sea off the Durham coast. Through this programme assets worth £2·5 billion have been added to the country's natural resources—should they be needed.

The only country producing coal economically—because of extremely advanced techniques—is the U.S., which is now shipping coal to markets as far away as Italy and Japan.

COCOA

Ghana, Brazil, the Cameroons, Togo and the Ivory Coast all suffered losses on cocoa during 1965 because of low prices caused by over production. The situation was specially serious in Ghana, where cocoa provides 60% of the national income. Much cocoa has been burned, but world output in 1966 is estimated to be 25% higher than in 1965.

Ghana and Nigeria now produce over 50% of the world's cocoa, a dramatic change from the days when Equador was the leading producer. Equador is now sixth largest.

COFFEE

World imports of coffee have been rising steadily and will probably reach 60m cwt in 1966. The U.S. is by far the largest importer and currently takes half the world's imports, but it has only the third largest consumption per head—about 17lb. The Swedes are the heaviest coffee drinkers (24lb per head), then the Danes (21 lb per head). British consumption, though only 3 lb per head, is growing faster than elsewhere. Britain was the 16th largest importer before 1939 but is now the 7th largest: East Africa, particularly Uganda, supplies more than half the British demands. About 75% of British imports of green coffee are now manufactured into instant coffee. The International Coffee Agreement has not been completely successful in maintaining prices at a level that many producers consider satisfactory because quotas have been set considerably above world demand for coffee.

Long term, it is impossible to forecast production accurately, because coffee is acutely sensitive to weather variations. Several producing countries, including Brazil, Colombia, Costa Rica, El Salvador, Angola and the Ivory Coast have opened or are planning to open factories for manufacturing instant coffee. There are now many substitutes for coffee, especially those derived from chicory, dried figs and malted cereals.

In an effort to support prices the Brazil government bought up half of 1965's crop. Colombia, dependent on coffee for 70% of its exports, has resorted to bartering it for goods that it lacks the money to buy.

COLOMBIA

461,606 sq m. Pop. 15·4m. The economy has deteriorated and will deteriorate further unless political unrest, inflation and tax evasion are curbed. Colombia is the world's second largest producer of coffee, which provides about 70% of export earnings. However, in 1965 and again in 1966 exports declined drastically. Efforts are being made to diversify agricultural products;

exports of meat, sugar, bananas and tobacco and cotton are growing. These and other minor exports yielded £42m in 1966, compared with £20m in 1964. Cattle are being exported to Italy and Peru. Production of petroleum, accounting for about a sixth of Colombia's exports, increased in 1965 and in 1966 new drilling and exploration projects were put in hand. Industrial development is continuing and recent projects include a fungicide plant, a polystyrene plant, a factory to extract oil from rice, and a paper mill. The Export-Import Bank has lent £1m to modernise a steel plant and France and West Germany will probably finance a second steel plant.

Colombia has greater potential than before realised. Rich mineral resources include gold, silver, iron ore and limestone. Japan's largest mining company, already mining copper in Peru and Chile, is to exploit mineral deposits in Colombia's so-called "California" area. Since the copper deposits there are not high-grade, it is assumed that hopes of finding gold and uranium influenced signing of the contracts. Colombia's coal reserves are now estimated to be the largest in South America.

Loans amounting to £30m have been received from various international agencies to finance hydro-electric schemes. The Inter-American Development Bank has recently lent £2m for a water supply system in Medellín. The government announced plans to expand and modernise the fishing industry. U.K. trade with Colombia is roughly at par—£4m annually each way.

COMMON MARKET

(European Economic Community, "The Six") Pop. 170m.

Labour shortages. Europe's labour shortage is acute, except in a few areas. It is especially serious in Western Germany,

Luxembourg and Holland and has eased only slightly in Belgium and France. Belgium is importing Turkish workers. Italy alone has provided 1·7m workers for Germany, France and Switzerland. Between 1956 and September 1964 Germany had imported 1m foreign workers and the total has since risen by many thousands. Ford of Germany has 7,000 foreign workers and Volkswagen has 4,500 Italians. Countries supplying the labour are Spain, Portugal, North Africa (especially Algeria), Yugoslavia, Greece, Turkey, India.

Competition for Beef. Common Market countries are competing strongly with Britain for beef. They need about 750,000 tons a year to meet the deficit in their own production. Total requirements by the Common Market countries are 4·3m tons. An increase in local production is forecast from 1967 onwards, but with rising standards of living the demand is increasing, particularly from Italy. The Six are buying now from Australia, Argentina, New Zealand, Uruguay and Yugoslavia.

Imports from Africa. During 1967 the European Common Market is pledged to abolish tariffs on all goods imported from their African associates—the 18 former French and Belgian colonies in Africa. Since January 1961 the Six have paid these African states about £250m in development aid.

The Common Market countries and the other countries of Europe have a total population of 300m and although increasingly affluent they own only one car for every 15 people. (The U.S. and Australia have one car to three people.) European car-makers will produce more than 8m cars in 1967 and expect to overtake U.S. production by 1970. Late in 1964 Europe had more than 50 automobile manufacturers but, for the sake of economy and competitiveness, mergers have been taking place ever since. Mergers are a new and profound feature of Europe's economic geography. They are affecting the transport, electrical, food processing and textile industries, among others.

Coal and steel are problems. The European Coal and Steel Community, when established in 1952, used coal for 75% of its fuel needs: the proportion is now only 35%, owing to increasing use of oil and other sources of power. Over-production of steel is also a problem. (See *Steel*.) Difficulties over coal and steel are threatening the unity of the Common Market.

COOK ISLANDS

Pop. 20,000. The first fruit-preserving factory has been built on the island of Rarotonga (pop. 8,000) and native fishermen have been equipped—by New Zealand—with modern boats to boost their catch.

COPPER

Total capacity of the world's copper mines, excluding the Soviet bloc, is about 4·75m short tons. North America, Western Europe and Japan account for 87% of the free world's copper supply. The world requires more copper—mostly for the electrical and plumbing industries and as a component of various alloys—than is being mined, despite increased production in Chile, the Congo, Zambia and the U.S. As a result, copper prices, always very volatile, have become very high.

The International Copper Research Association, Inc., with its head office in New York and a European office in London, is supported by almost all the copper-producing companies in the world and is concerned with finding new uses for copper. In many countries, notably Australia, New Zealand, Finland, Holland and the U.S. (Florida) a large tonnage of copper is consumed annually by the fertiliser industry for incorporation in fertiliser mixtures for application to copper-deficient soils.

A series of trials have now established, too, that feeding of a high level of copper to pigs significantly improves growth rate and food conversion efficiency. Copper sulphate is being used to control algae on farm ponds, reservoirs and drainage canals and to destroy the snail hosts of the liver fluke and bilharzia parasites, which are major scourges. In 1966 about 52,000 miles of copper tubing was supplied to the building industry in Britain.

During 1966 the U.S. government restricted exports of all kinds of copper to prevent price increases in the U.S.

The U.K. is the largest exporter of copper semi-manufactures in the world, but the prospects for increased direct exports are not encouraging because of the expansion of local manufacture in countries such as Australia, South Africa and India. In addition there is intense competition from Australian, Canadian and Italian manufacturers, notably inside the British Commonwealth which, until recently, was supplied from Britain.

Copper mines are being developed in Khetri, Rajasthan; in the southernmost part of the Ural Mountains and at Chambishi, Zambia.

COSTA RICA

19,653 sq m. Pop. 1·4m. Exports are increasing and include a wide variety of goods. The future is promising provided any fall in the value of coffee exports is counterbalanced by a growth of other exports. Industrial development has continued. Cotton cultivation has increased so much that the 1965 yield was 80% higher than the 1964 yield. About 85% of the crop goes to Japan. A survey of timber resources has shown that timber could become even more valuable than coffee as an export commodity. During 1964–5 more than 150 new industries were established. Industries include food processing, rubber products, shoes and clothing, wood, electrical and mechanical products. An insecticide plant, a tyre plant and a freeze-dry food plant will be in operation during 1967. Three industrial zones are to be set up. The government has signed a 25-year contract with an American company to mine bauxite. A canal link between Puerto Limon and a new oil refinery, and a large water system for the capital, San José, are under construction. A new HEP scheme will be in operation by 1969. The Instituto Cistaticense de Electricedad will invest £35m in HEP schemes before 1975. New trading partners are Japan, Nationalist China and Argentina.

COTTON

There are very few new areas for cotton growing though Russia is growing it most successfully in southern areas around the Caspian and Black Seas. For the first time, Australia is a cotton-growing country, the producing area being the Ord River Irrigation Area in north Western Australia. The present area is small, but will grow. In parts of Africa cotton areas have been expanding and yields have been higher, following better growing methods. Cotton-growing experiments in New Guinea have been successful.

Despite synthetics, world trade in raw cotton and in cotton textiles has increased. India, Pakistan, Japan and Hong Kong are producing such large quantities of cheap cotton textiles that the longer-established producers have imposed tariff barriers. A modern textile industry is growing up at Fort-Archambault, the cotton-growing centre in the African republic of Chad. By the middle of 1966 the industry was producing nearly 10m sq yds annually. The German Development Company is providing 35% of the capital.
(See *Costa Rica*.)

COUNCIL OF EUROPE

The Council, which has its headquarters in Strasbourg, is the parliamentary and governmental forum where proposals for a more efficient organisation for Europe are initiated. It has 19 member nations. Its work is complex, and affects more than geography. Its influence on economic geography is profound and through liaison committees it has been able to influence the industrial development of Europe and economic relations among the member states. Founded in 1949, the Council has so far been mentioned in very few geography textbooks.

CUBA

44,178 sq m. Pop. 7·4m. The 1965 sugar harvest was the third largest in Cuba's history—6,050m tons—but the economy is unstable. Much of the crop was not sold because of a world sugar glut and it brought in only £20m—half the 1964 figure. Because of drought the 1966 crop was 0·5m tons, much less than in 1965. China has reduced her exports of rice to Cuba and the coffee crop for 1965 was only 25,000 tons—40% less than in 1959 (the year President Castro assumed leadership). Because of the poor quality of capital equipment supplied by the Soviet bloc, Cuba would like to buy equipment from Western Europe, but is short of foreign exchange. This has led to the cancellation of an order for a French firm to build a £5½m plant for making fertiliser, caustic soda and insecticide. The Soviet bloc buys two-thirds of Cuba's exports and gives Cuba £125m annually in aid money, while Russia directly buys 2m tons of sugar. About 70% of British exports to Cuba consist of machinery and transport equipment, while sugar accounts for over three-quarters of the value of British imports. For several years Cuba must depend on the willingness of its trading partners to give generous credit, as the country tries to diversify its agriculture by growing tropical fruits, coffee and rearing beef cattle.

CURRENCY

In February 1966 the Australian units of currency became the dollar and cent which superseded the pound and shilling. The dollar is equal to 10 shillings. Until mid-1967, however, the old and new currencies will circulate together.

CZECHOSLOVAKIA

49,000 sq m. Pop. 15m. Between 1966–70 the Government will invest much money in agricultural reform schemes, the main one being mechanisation. The engineering, food and consumer goods industries are to be modernised. Czechoslovakia is now importing large quantities of raw materials and machinery to process them: the equipment alone costs more than £300m annually.

The chemical industry is expanding, mainly with petro-chemicals at Most and with fertilisers, acids, pharmaceuticals and photographic products near Ústí. The nation's old-established textile industry has undergone changes following new economic policies, with quantities of raw materials coming from the Soviet. The mills in northern Bohemia have been closed and new ones opened in southern Bohemia, Moravia and Slovakia. The Danube is of increasing import-

ance since the ports of Bratislava and Komárno now handle
heavy freight from the Soviet Union. In the period 1966–70
Czechoslovakia and the Soviet Union plan to exchange goods
valued at £4,000m.

D

DAMS

Late in March 1966 the king of Thailand dedicated the Nam Pong £10m dam across a tributary of the great Mekong River. This was part of an ambitious German-financed and German-built effort to convert the Mekong's torrent into a source of prosperity. The dam, 300 miles north-east of Bangkok, will store irrigation water for 115 sq m. of Thai farms and will provide electric power for Thailand and neighbouring Laos. Laos, South Vietnam, Thailand and Cambodia will all benefit from schemes along the Mekong's 2,625-mile length. In addition to Nam Pong Dam, five other dams, with associated power and irrigation projects, are being built on Mekong tributaries.

A dam and power station are being built on the River Awash, 62 miles south of Addis Ababa to provide for the capital's increasing electricity requirements. Planned by a German firm and financed by the World Bank, the project will be carried out by a French firm.

The European Investment Bank has granted a large loan for the building of the vast Keban dam in Anatolia. Further funds were provided by West Germany, France and Switzerland.

Work has begun on the big El Chocon-Los Cerillos dam in Southern Argentina. The 300m dollar project envisages a reservoir, 289 square miles in extent, electricity production of 1·2 million kilowatts and irrigation of 1,729,700 acres of land.

In the Tien-Shan Mountains, near Alma Ata, capital of the Russian republic of Kazakhstan, 5,000 tons of dynamite were

80

exploded to displace 2½m cubic metres of rock to form a dam 280 feet high across the valley of the River Almatinka. The dam diverts the river so that the water flows through a two-mile tunnel. One effect is to save damage, previously caused each year at Alma Ata by spring floods.
(See *Afghanistan, Argentina, Australia, Austria, India.*)

DENMARK

16,000 sq m. Pop. 4·7m. Agricultural products accounted for 35%, by value, of exports during 1965. Normally bacon alone takes up about 11% of total export earnings, but prices have been threatened by a rise of about 14% in pig production and thousands of carcases had to be cold-stored. To obviate any further excess production the price of barley was increased to induce farmers to sell the grain rather than feed it to their pigs. Denmark's main markets for agricultural produce remain Britain and West Germany, although exports to West Germany have fallen off sharply. Industry now contributes nearly twice as much to the national income as does agriculture, and industrial sales are growing at a faster rate: in 1965 they increased 17% over the figures for 1964. Exports of chemicals, machinery and appliances, ships and boats, canned meat, animal and vegetable oils and fats, and metal manufactures have all increased. However, the large quantity of imports leaves Denmark with a deficit. Britain is Denmark's main market, taking about a quarter of the exports, but West Germany is Denmark's main supplier (20%). By the end of 1966 all British goods were allowed into Denmark free of tariff.

DIAMONDS

Industrial diamonds can now be made. In 1966 a Dutch chemist, Mudde, produced them in a process which involves submitting carbon in a steel mould to a pressure of 400,000 atmospheres. He claims that he can produce diamonds at little more than a tenth of their present price—about 18*s* a carat. (See *Guyana*.)

DROUGHT

The seriousness of drought in modern times can be seen by the experience of Australia which in the drought of 1965–6 lost at least 15·5m sheep and 1·36m cattle. Most of the losses occurred in New South Wales, the rest in Queensland. (See *Weather*.) Arable crops have also suffered. The Australian wheat crop for 1966 was reduced by one third—a loss of 185m bushels. India, too, was drought-devastated: in places, such as Uttar Pradesh, the wheat yield was reduced by half.

E

EARTHQUAKES

Chile. Of the thousands of tremors recorded each year about 15% occur in Chile. In May 1965 an earthquake of a minute's duration shook 130,000 sq m. In Valparaiso, the major seaport, 30% of the buildings were damaged. A large earth dam gave way at the copper town of El Cobre and 200 people were buried in mud. Damage amounted to £40m. In 1966 China, Turkey, Iran, Iraq and Uganda also had severe earthquakes.

EASTERN EUROPE
(See also individual countries)

Industrial production in Eastern Europe has been adversely affected by poor workmanship. Buyers have rejected large quantities of Hungarian bicycles, sewing-machines, textiles. The same country has been unable to sell poor quality shirts and shoes to the West. In Poland in 1966 4m pairs of shoes had to be reclassified as sub-standard, as well as 19% of radio and TV sets. Czechoslovakia and, to a lesser extent, Bulgaria have suffered similarly. One consequence is that Western countries are increasing exports to the countries of the Soviet bloc. Austria has sold an entire steel plant to Czechoslovakia; France is building an automobile assembly plant for East Germany and the British Motor Corporation is building one in

Poland. Near Ploeşti in Rumania a U.S. company has started a £7m cracking plant. Nevertheless, Eastern Europe still buys only 4% of Western Europe's exports, though this percentage is likely to rise. West Germany is by far the leading Western supplier. Britain, the second largest Western Europe supplier in 1964, was overtaken by Italy and France in 1965 and seems unlikely to recover her former position.

At the end of October 1966 it was clear that the countries of Eastern Europe had two things dominantly in common: ambitious plans for tourism and a desire to become more industrially competitive within their own borders.

EAST GERMANY
(German Democratic Republic)

41,479 sq m. Pop. 17·3m. East Germany is the major producer in the Soviet bloc and still has the highest living standards of any Communist country. Its output is only one-fifth that of West Germany but East Germany describes itself, falsely, as the world's 10th biggest industrial power. However, production is increasing by 5% annually. Four-fifths of the country's production is in industrial goods—petrochemicals, computers, heavy machines. Russia takes 50% of East German exports; West Germany takes 10%. Russia is helping East Germany to build the "Communist Ruhr" along the Polish border. At Schwedt on the Oder River is a £35m chemical plant; Schwedt is the terminus of a 2,500-mile oil pipeline from the Urals. At Eisenhüttenstadt (Iron City) is a fully automatic steel plant, with 9,000 workers. At Cottbus a £270m brown coal lignite plant will be complete by 1970. It will make and pump gas over 1,500 miles of pipeline to every part of East Germany as the main source of heating and power-station supply. This will replace the coal imported from West Germany. HEP stations are being completed on the Saale River.

EGYPT

386,110 sq m. Pop. 29m. Under the first development programme, 1960–5, national income rose by 40%. A new plan began in July 1965 and under it Egypt hopes to increase her income by half to about £2,200m. Russia has granted Egypt £100m to help finance the Five-Year Plan; Poland has contributed £7m for a new aluminium plant, Hungary £15m for equipment and plant. Kuwait has lent £35m and France has given £20m in exchange for French property seized at the time of the Suez crisis in 1956. However, for the present Egypt's economy is strained: half the cotton crop must be sent annually to Russia to pay for arms, factories and work on the Aswan Dam. Cotton output rose by 13% in the 1965 season and by a further 10% in 1966.

Rice production is increasing greatly, but food has been short and Egypt has had to import American wheat. During the first half of 1966 the U.S. shipped almost £20m of surplus food to Egypt. In 1967 the completion of the Aswan Dam will add 2m acres of cultivable land, which is at present only 4% of the total area. But if the present rate of population increase continues—2·9% annually—there will be less cultivable land per head when the Aswan Dam project is finished than there is today. (Egypt's family planning council offers husbands 50 piastres (8*s*) to take their wives to centres dispensing free birth control devices.)

The Suez Canal dues have increased to £66m annually— 19,000 ships. Egypt is establishing a free port at Port Said and to encourage foreign investment the government is granting concessions. Already Japan, Spain, Denmark, Mexico, Holland and Belgium have offered to build factories. Early in 1966 a World Bank mission visited Egypt to study the financing of the development programme and the expansion of projects in the Port Said scheme. Oil is becoming an increasing source of revenue in Egypt. By the end of 1966 production had commenced from a new oilfield in the Red Sea and other new sources have been found in the Western Desert. Tourism is already bringing in £50m annually and this figure is increasing. Somewhat surprisingly, the U.S., West Germany and Britain—in that order—are Egypt's main suppliers, but Britain's share of the trade has fallen to little more than half what it was in 1963. In a normal year the credit balance is £20m.

The New Valley Scheme. Little publicised abroad, the ambitious New Valley scheme may eventually prove almost as important as the Aswan High Dam project. The scheme aims to link the five Western Desert oases into a major population-supporting area. The oases are Siwa, Bahariya, Farafra, Dakhla and Khârga. The combined population today is 50,000: some planners believe the area could support 2m. Until recently there were doubts about the water supplies under the New Valley oases, but international scientific research has established that subterranean seepage replenishes the supplies. American and German drilling teams have sunk hundreds of artesian wells and a pilot area of about 65,000 acres has been irrigated. Russians, Yugoslavs, French and Italians have also been helping in the project. Some people are already calling the New Valley Egypt's "second lung". Egypt's difficulty is in inducing peasant farmers to move from the Nile Valley to the new region. Parts of the New Valley scheme are already functioning, but it will not be complete until 1970.

EIRE
(Republic of Ireland)

26,600 sq m. Pop. 2·9m. The Second Programme for Economic Expansion 1964–70 was designed to increase industrial output by 7% annually and on average this has been achieved, with the largest advances in drink, tobacco, chemicals and building materials. In Waterford and Galway industrial estates are to be established. Irish economic policy is to expand the trading area, particularly for manufactured goods. Eire depends on Britain to take 70% of her exports and it is possible that a Free Trade Area will be established between Britain and Eire. Irish economy is so dependent on trade with Britain that the growth rate of the Irish gross national product has risen and fallen with that of Britain. Eire sells almost twice as much to Northern Ireland as she buys.

Despite all Eire's difficulties it is significant that Irish industrial output has risen twice as fast as industrial output in Britain. By contrast, agricultural output has been much less buoyant.

It is interesting to note the growth of the Guinness company, which now employs 4,300 people, more than any employer apart from the government. Indirectly, the company supports 26,000 employees of 14,500 public houses and 16,000 Irish farmers depend on Guinness to buy 100,000 tons of barley annually. In Britain, the company's best export market, served by a fleet of Guinness ships, surtaxes have been costing Guinness £500,000 a year. To help balance this, the company has bought several British confectionery firms and a chain of shops.

EL SALVADOR

7,722 sq m. Pop. 3·05m. Sugar production is increasing rapidly with the 1966 crop nearly three times that of 1964. Production of maize and beans has declined. Industrialisation is increasing: in the period 1964–6 no fewer than 290 new firms were established. New industries include clothing, paper products, plastics, steel tanks and pipes, metal containers, food processing, rolled steel, glassware. There is motor car assembly plant; chemical and pharmaceutical factories are planned for 1966–7 and a new thermo-electric plant has been built at Acajutla. Roads are being improved.

EQUADOR

226,000 sq m. Pop. 4·9m. An Equadorian development plan, evolved with the help of advisers from 19 countries, comprises 40 projects with a total cost of £115m. The ambitious plan, supposed to be completed by 1973, may not be entirely fulfilled, but there is great emphasis on the development of industry. Such a step is certainly necessary. At present bananas account for over half the country's export earnings. Equador has become the largest exporter of bananas, but the market has been unsteady. Coffee and cocoa exports rose considerably in 1965 and will probably continue to rise. In the Guayas River Basin sugar cultivation is being extended. Manufacturing industries already developed include steel and electrical products, cement, glassware, agricultural equipment, food canning, making of insecticides. Irrigation and hydro-electric schemes will further improve the country's economy, while improved communications are opening up a very large region in Morona-Santiago province.

(The difficulty of obtaining accurate figures for areas of countries is shown in the case of Equador: I have found 32 different figures ranging from 166,000 to 320,000 sq m.)

EUROPEAN FREE TRADE ASSOCIATION

By the end of 1966 all tariffs on industrial goods within EFTA had disappeared. Since this is one of the major aims of EFTA it is important to appreciate what has been achieved by this union of Austria, Denmark, Finland (associate member), Norway, Portugal, Sweden, Switzerland and Britain. It is not generally understood that EFTA was not intended to be a rival system to the Common Market. Unlike Common Market countries those of EFTA have no common external tariff: each member runs its own trade relations outside EFTA, though there is a good deal of co-operation among member states in international negotiations. One advantage of the free trade area system was that Britain could leave her Commonwealth preference system intact. EFTA's 98m people are among the most highly dependent on trade in the world. Each person, on average, buys £120 of imported goods, including those from other EFTA countries. (Each Common Market citizen buys about £88 worth from outside his own country and each American £35.) In total, EFTA now buys 20% of world imports and sells 17%. Income per head is 10% above that in the Common Market. Britain accounts for over half EFTA's trade with outside countries, but her share of all trade within EFTA is generally 29%, about that of Sweden. It is important to note that while EFTA doubles Britain's "home" market, it increases that of each other member more than ten-fold because of Britain's much greater population. There has been a remarkable increase in trade among the eight countries since the Area was instituted. Intra-EFTA trade increased by well over 20%. Britain's trade with her partners is largely manufactures being exchanged for food and raw materials. Ireland and Yugoslavia have shown interest in joining EFTA, but a more important step is the attempt to link the economies of the Common Market with those of EFTA.

Towards the end of 1966 the EFTA Secretary-General said that difficulties over agriculture—e.g. lack of a co-ordinated policy to plan production—is the main economic obstacle in bringing about a wider European market.

F

FAROE ISLANDS

540 sq m. Pop. 36,000. With only four per cent of the land cultivable, the Faroes have had to concentrate on the fishing industry, which is now worth about £15m in boats and shore installations. Main markets are Britain, the U.S., Norway, Spain, Italy and Brazil. Despite the harsh climate, the population is increasing.

FINLAND

130,165 sq m. Pop. 4·6m. An associate member of the European Free Trade Association, Finland is developing steadily, but does have one major problem: it has been cutting too much timber—and timber provides more than 70% of total export earnings. The government has introduced an intensive re-afforestation programme with a 2% decrease in cutting. Nevertheless, stocks of suitable trees are diminishing. Britain is Finland's chief customer, with a credit balance of nearly £50m in 1965. The money comes mostly from timber products, iron and steel, non-ferrous metals, metal manufactures, non-electric machinery, transport equipment, textile fibres. Finland is trying to diversify her industry by producing wood and metal products, chemicals, footwear, paper, electrical machinery and textiles.

The future growth of Finnish economy is largely linked with imports from the Common Market. These imports include iron and steel and other metal products, engineering machinery, electrical equipment, motor vehicles, sanitation, heating and lighting appliances, precision instruments. Finland has been importing as much as 40% of these products from Common Market countries. If the Finnish pulp and paper industry were to remain mainly as a supplier of raw material and semi-finished goods the country's capacity to import would fall and its economic growth would slow down.

An important outlet for Finland's timber industry is being modernised. It is the Saima Canal, built more than a century ago to connect the Saima Lake system with the Gulf of Finland at the Russian port of Vyborg. The cost will be great, and ice will close the canal for two to three months annually but the re-opening of the canal, scheduled for 1967–8, could solve many Finnish problems. Seven ports may be built on the system, with consequent attraction of new industries.

Finnish Railways are modernising their trains. New engines including 2,800 hp Diesel locomotives; passenger trains and 1,000 new goods wagons are to be bought.

FISHING

Few industries are developing as rapidly as the fishing industry and few are as competitive. In many oceans fish "wars" have occurred or are still in progress. Since the beginning of the century the fishing yield has increased more than tenfold, to its present total of 48m tons. By 1970 the catch will probably reach 61m tons. More than 200 countries send fishing boats to sea, but 48 countries account for the bulk of the catch. In all, about 5m commercial fishermen are at work. Including lobsters, molluscs, etc. the total world annual catch amounts to 100 billion lb. Individual catches are: Japan, 15 billion lb; Peru 11·6; Communist China 11·1, USSR 8·5; U.S. 6·5; Norway 3·3; Canada 2·3; Spain 2·2; India 2·1; Britain 2·0. Much of the fish is marketed fresh—34·1 billion lb.

Disputes. Intensified fishing has led to many new disputes. The older ones, such as that between Britain and Iceland, are well known. Later troubles have occurred between: Russia and Japan—salmon off Hokkaido; U.S. and Canada in conflict with Japan—salmon north of the Aleutian Islands; Equador and Peru in conflict with the U.S.—tuna off the coasts of the two South American countries; Mexico and the U.S.—shrimp in the Gulf of Mexico; Brazil and France—lobsters off the central Brazil coast. Trouble is always imminent on the Grand Banks of Newfoundland where 15 nations are fishing.

Sockeye Salmon Problem. The U.S. has been acutely embarrassed by the sockeye salmon problem, a vital industry in the fishing towns of northern Washington state and coastal Alaska. Each year the local industry catches up to 6m sockeye (generally 2 ft long) which account for the area's £17m salmon catch and bring higher prices than other salmon. When the U.S., Canada and Japan instituted their North Pacific Fisheries Treaty in 1953, North American negotiators set 175 degrees West longitude as the eastward limit for Japanese fishermen. They have recently been surprised to learn that the sockeye salmon swims out around the Aleutian Islands for more than 3,000 miles—on a course that takes it well into Japanese waters. The Japanese, with more than 200 boats constantly working on their side of the 175th meridian, are catching probably 7m salmon. At least 12m of the estimated total of 27m must be spared for spawning, and so the U.S. authorities have had arbitrarily to restrict the American catch. Those sockeye which evade the Japanese nets on the return part of their elliptical course spawn in such rivers as the Nushagak, Egegik, Ugashik, Kvichak and Naknek.

Techniques. Fish provides only 12% of the supply of animal protein consumed by the human race and only about 15% of the world's edible fish stock is being fully exploited. However, many new techniques are now being followed or are in the experiment stage.

Probably the most hopeful method of fishing is the electric "net" evolved by the Germans Hans Rump and Karl Ulrichs. With their first test the Germans eliminated all scepticism about their "electrotaxis" methods. The process is simple: an electrode with an impulse of up to 20,000 amperes is let down into the water and fish within a radius of 80 feet are attracted to it, to be drawn into a suction pipe where they are killed by stronger electric shock. The method works well in the open seas (fishing by electricity in lakes and rivers is not new) and a boat can take in 2,000 lb of fish a minute. Apart from other advantages, fishermen normally working under arduous, extreme and dangerous conditions, can now catch in five minutes what they would formerly take in two hours. A further benefit of electrotaxis is that it can be so adjusted that young fish can be kept away from it.

Owing to new methods—use of helicopters and submarines, for instance—Russia's catches are constantly increasing. Off Newfoundland Russian fishermen are taking 10 times more fish than local fishermen. They are taking large quantities off the coasts of Japan and South Africa and are now operating in the middle of the Indian Ocean. Soviet specialists have explored the possibility of fishing in the Pacific and Atlantic as far down as 3,000 feet, but they have not yet published their findings. Karachi, Pakistan, has one of the most interesting and ambitious fishing projects. The "fish harbour project" takes the form of a complete and self-contained fishing community, the people of which build their own ships and gear and process and distribute their own fish. It is building up steadily with bigger ships, more distant waters and growing markets. One market is the U.S., to which Karachi sells large deep-frozen prawns. *Fish-farming.* Methods of farming the fish of the sea are being investigated by British scientists. They aim also to produce fish of standard size and weight to simplify the equipment for cutting and processing the fish for packaging and for conversion into fish fingers.

The scientists are enclosing about five acres of sea off the coast of Argyll in Scotland. This pilot plot will provide information about the conditions needed for rearing fish. The "fence" will be created by means of nets, electrical devices or ultrasonics.

Other sites suitable for fish farms that have already been surveyed total 2,000 acres, an area capable of supporting 30m fish, or 15,000 fish per acre.

Scientists have already succeeded in hatching and rearing plaice to postage stamp size at the Marine Laboratory in Lowestoft. Other experiments have been taking place on the coast of Aberdeen in Scotland, and the Isle of Man, and Strathclyde University has been given a £34,000 grant for research work by the British White Fish Authority.

Only in recent years has fish farming been exploited as a crop for rural Africans, partly because the United Nations Special Fund paid for fish farming to be developed at Kariba and at Lake Tanganyika. Zambia has eight large fish dams and 1,000 smaller ones scattered over the territory and they produce about 700 tons a year, small, so far, compared with the 40,000 tons caught in natural waters. The Fisheries Department stocks the various ponds with a total of about 125,000 live fish a year. The department advises Africans where and how to build a pond, which may be only a twentieth of an acre. About 20 lb of fish are placed in a pond of a tenth of an acre and within a year this weight rises to about 120 lb. Pond-owners now have an all-year source of food and they crop during the rains when market fish is scarce and prices high.

Demands for stock-fish comes in frequently to the two departmental fish farms at Chilanga and Mwekera. Mwekera has 40 ponds covering 16 acres and raises fish up to 3,000 lb per acre per year. Important experiments made by the Zambian experts are likely to be used as a basis by other countries.

Fleets. The fishing fleets of Russia, East Germany and Poland have been developed at the same high speed as their merchant fleets and are capable of operating at long distances from their home ports and of staying at sea for long periods. The Russian fleet includes 120 large freezer trawlers that fish, process and store up to 600 tons of finished products each cruise. Between 1954 and 1964 the Russian trawler fleet increased fourfold and today she has the world's largest and most modern seagoing fishing fleet. The Polish Gdansil yard is specialising in building the *B.64* type of depot-processing ship, 10,000 tons, one of the largest craft in the world of this kind. East Germany has at least seven factory trawlers of the *Peter Nell* class. In place of the conventional derrick the ship has a crane off her stern capable of handling a trawl of up to 25 tons of fish. The loading hatch can be opened and closed automatically from the bridge: the equipment includes a fish-meal plant and a new type of shoal detector.

Indian Ocean Research. The International Indian Ocean Expedition, which concluded its work in 1966, will take some time to evaluate all the data collected by the 40 ships from 13 nations, but one important result has already been announced. Rich stocks of fish exist off the coasts of Muscat and 'Oman on the Arabian Peninsula, as well as off Somalia and Burma.

FORMOSA
(Taiwan or Nationalist China)

13,850 sq m. Pop. 12·4m. This country is another success story, and its economic geography is vastly different from that usually pictured. The Nationalist Chinese have increased crop yields by 100% by thorough land reform. Agricultural exports now amount to £100m. Formosa's land reform means, basically, that land ownership is not in the hands of a few rapacious landlords and moneylenders but that farms are now owned by their occupiers. Government-owned land has been sold at reasonable prices. Now only about 7% of Formosa's 600,000 farmers are tenants.

However, agriculture does not dominate the economy. Since 1952 no fewer than 15,500 new factories have been built and about 26,000 handicraft enterprises set up. In this way 1m new jobs have been created: another 600,000 men and women are serving in the army. Industrial growth rate is about 20·5%—one of the highest in the world. Formosa's trade balance shows a surplus of £20m, through exports of pineapples (Formosa is now the world's largest exporter with 2·5m cases of canned pineapple), sugar, textiles, timber, chemicals, agricultural produce and fish. Growing of mushrooms is a new industry and at least 1m cases are exported annually.

It would be a mistake to suppose that Formosa will ever be a major industrial nation, but its rate of development can be shown by the fact that it is second only to that of Japan.

Much of Formosa's prosperity is due to the vast sums of money given by the U.S.—1·8 billion dollars since 1949. U.S. companies have also built factories in Formosa: they include Socony Mobil Oil; Allied Chemicals (now operating with a Chinese partner); a £7m fertiliser factory; American Cyanamid (an antibiotics plant); Proctor and Gamble (detergents); Atlas Chemical (industrial dynamite); Singer Sewing Machines; Harvey Aluminium; Gulf Oil. Apart from the U.S., Formosa's main trading partners are Japan, Western Germany, South Vietnam and Hong Kong.

FRANCE

212,700 sq m. Pop. 48·7m. Income per head in France is now £490 (Britain, £489). France remains Britain's fourth largest market in Europe and there is room for expansion. To stimulate industrial investment and to recharge the economy the government has taken the unusual step of issuing a State loan of 1,000m francs to provide loan funds for investment. The metallurgical industry has received 300m francs; the car, chemical and electronics industries have also benefited. French economy generally is stable and is likely to remain so under the Fifth Economic Plan 1966–70, which provides for price increases averaging only $1\frac{1}{2}\%$ annually.

As usual, French farming is the economy's uncertain feature. During 1965 and 1966 the government made moves which threatened the stability of the Common Market, but in 1966 the vice president of the French National Federation of Farmers' Syndicates said: "Belonging to the European Community is a matter of life or death to our agriculture." France has sold wheat to Russia—300,000 tons in 1965. Deliveries were made to Baltic and Black Sea ports in cargo-lots of 60,000 tons.

Late in 1966 it became clear that France has the strongest balance of payments surplus in the world. In October 1966 during a British Week in Lyons about 450 British firms took the first step towards tapping the considerable market in the Rhône Valley, where industrialisation is increasing. One of the few things decreasing is income from tourism: in 1966, for the first time in history, French tourists abroad paid out more money than France received in tourist revenue. (See *Alsace, Canals*.)

G

GEOLOGY

Following the disastrous Alaskan earthquake of 1964, geologists at Anchorage have been studying an underlying layer of thick clay from 10 to 30 feet thick. They have reported that during the three minutes of the earthquake's violence some of this clay turned into liquid, thus initiating landslides. To minimise damage from future Alaskan earthquakes Army engineers are experimenting with a technique already used in Norway: they are forcing electrodes into the layer of clay and passing high-amperage currents among the electrodes to reorientate the clay particles. Scientists are planning, too, to pump enough calcium salts into the clay to bind its particles together by electrolytic action, to make the clay more viscous, resistant to shock and no longer thixotropic.

GEOMORPHOLOGY

GONDWANALAND (Wegener Theory)

Alfred Wegener's theory of Continental drift, evolved more than 50 years ago, has been reinforced with fresh evidence. Wegener suggested that 200m years ago there was a single great land mass, Gondwanaland, on the earth's surface, that it had split and that the fragments drifted apart to form the continents. Professor Patrick Blackett's recent theory (1963) is based on the premise, not new in itself, that convection currents are at work in the earth's interior and that though they move at a rate of only an inch or so a year they are sufficient to account for continuous movement of the earth's various land masses. By studying rock magnetism Professor Blackett and others have shown that South America, South Africa, Australia and India were probably once closer together and much nearer to the South Pole. This accounts for the glaciation they all appear to have undergone about 200m years ago. What is now Northern Europe was probably much closer to the equator—hence the tropical forests from which British coal supplies were formed.

GEOPHYSICS

An important development has been the drastic revision of estimates of the temperature of the earth's core following calculations by an American, Professor George Kennedy. His research should provide new insight into the present structure of the earth and its ancient geological activity. Lindemann's Law has long been used to determine melting points of iron and other substances that increase in volume as they melt. Using data from controlled laboratory tests, Professor Kennedy plotted the melting temperatures of 50 different substances against their density at varying temperatures. He found a direct relationship between melting point and density, not melting point and pressure. Under Lindemann's Law the temperature in the earth's core was said to be 13,500 degrees F. Professor Kennedy has proved that it is only 6,700 degrees F. His findings will alter most theories about the thermal history of the earth and should help to explain how heat escapes from the earth's interior.

The Soviet spaceship *Luna 10* has apparently confirmed in April 1966, that the earth's magnetic field extends as far as the moon.

A group of Columbia University scientists announced in July 1966 that the periodic "flipping" of the earth's magnetic field may play a major part in the evolution of terrestrial life. Within a period of 10,000 years the north and south magnetic poles change places; the Columbia University team has shown that the most recent reversal occurred about 700,000 years ago and that at this time certain species of algae and protozoa underwent marked changes. They say that a new reversal could occur in a few hundred to a few thousand years and that Man may undergo changes as a result.

GHANA

91,843 sq m. Pop. 7·6m. During 1965 Ghana tried to borrow money from Britain, the U.S., France, Italy, West Germany, Japan and Holland. Eventually the country succeeded in an application to the International Monetary Fund, provided several conditions were met. This shows the instability of Ghana's economy, though improvement is certain under new government. Many State-run enterprises have lost much money. One remedy has been to decide to sell Ghana's cocoa for hard cash and no longer on a barter basis, for Ghana's prosperity is largely dependent on cocoa prices. The long term outlook is good.

The Volta dam, about 70 miles north of Accra, is now complete. Ghana's whole development plan is based on the dam and the HEP it will produce. Half the power generated will be used by the aluminium smelter at Tema, about 18 miles east of Accra. Here, too, an £18m harbour is in its final stages of development. The largest artificial harbour in Africa, Tema should help Ghana's economy. The lake behind the Volta dam is to be used for a fishing industry.

Other very recent signs of commercial development include a large chicken hatchery near Winneba, a distillery at Kumasi, a textile plant at Tema, a glass factory at Aboso, an agricultural tools plant at Cape Coast (financed by Poland) and a sugar refinery. In the north the State Meat Corporation expects to produce 9,000 tins of corned beef and luncheon meat per day. Britain has an annual credit balance of about £15m in her trade with Ghana.

GREECE

41,328 sq m. Pop. 8·6m. Greece has more than doubled its gross national product, industrial production and personal income since 1946 but the economy remains unsteady with many problems caused by weak agriculture which the government has had to subsidise heavily. This had led to inflation and over production. For instance, the subsidy paid to wheat farmers has been almost twice the world market price, with the result that at the end of 1965 the government had 1m tons surplus. Another effect of the high prices for wheat is a 50% drop in cotton production, which had for several years been a profitable export.

Greece is anxious to bring its economy into line with the Common Market, of which it is an associate member, so as to gain access to the Common Market and to agricultural aid. Money from tourism, a growing industry, from shipping and deposits sent home by Greeks living abroad, helps to meet the large trade deficit. Britain is one of Greece's largest suppliers and with Greece needing industrial equipment Britain could sell even more. Greece's industrial leanings are towards fruit and vegetable processing, citrus juice canning, bottling of wines and processing of olives, olive oil and dairy products. The biggest single foreign investment ever made in Greece is a £65m industrial complex near Salonika—the Salonika Industrial Development Plan—which includes projects by three U.S. companies. The refinery section produces 50,000 barrels of petrol a day. Esso is also building a 200,000 tons a year ammonia plant.

However, both these are relatively insignificant compared with the £45m aluminium factory on the Bay of Antikyra in the shadow of Mount Parnassus. The plant not only gives Greece a new industry but by the end of 1966 was expected to double the country's industrial exports. A French-Greek-American combine called Aluminium of Greece built the plant and France's biggest aluminium maker, Pechiney, holds 50% of the shares. The bauxite is mined locally—its find in 1964 surprised geologists—and the plant was built at Antikyra because of deep-harbour facilities. Power comes from a new HEP station at Kremastá. The factory's ultimate annual production target is 72,000 tons of aluminium, only 15% of which will be used in Greece.

The islands of Greece are being steadily de-populated and their only chance of being revitalised is with tourism. The tourist potential in the islands is virtually untapped, although since 1960 the total number of foreign visitors to Greece has increased by more than 100,000 a year. Tourism is said to represent nearly 40% of the country's exports, but this figure is suspect.

GREENLAND

840,000 sq m. Pop. 40,000. Denmark is to spend another £200m over the next 10 years as part of her policy of industrialising the Eskimos. Priority in the plan will be given to ocean fishing vessels. Fishing is, as yet, Greenland's most important industry but the Greenlanders have at present only a 10% share of the total catch made around their coasts. Geologists are now systematically mapping the large deposits of niobium, beryllium and uranium the country is known to possess—apart from the cryolite which Greenland has been exporting for some years. The population growth is rapid: it should reach 50,000 in 1967 and will have doubled in 20 years.

GUATEMALA

42,042 sq m. Pop. 4·3m. Economic expansion continues but is less steady than in other central American countries. However, exports have reached record levels, despite pest damage to the 1964–5 coffee crop. Cotton is increasing steadily and is expected to reach 0·5m bales in 1968. Production of rubber is almost doubling annually and industrial production is increasing by 5% yearly. The Development Plan for 1965–9 involves spending £150m, of which 25% will go on roads and 20% on agriculture.

GUINEA

96,865 sq m. Pop. 4m. This country has serious economic problems and depends largely on the £85m a year paid to it by Russia, Communist China and the U.S. The major American contribution is £5m worth of rice. An American-built truck-assembly plant, a Russian-built dairy, and a West German-built slaughter-house have all failed recently. The country's backwardness is specially noticeable in relation to the success of its neighbour—the Ivory Coast.

GUYANA
(formerly British Guiana)

83,000 sq m. Pop. 0·7m. Despite political unrest, Guyana's four main money-earners—bauxite (world's fourth largest producer), timber, rice and sugar—are bringing in more money than ever before. New irrigation schemes have opened up large new tracts for rice and sugar and other crops. The administration is well aware of the danger of relying on a few crops and in recent years has given much attention to expanding the production of rice, and experiments with coffee and bananas have been successful. Guyana today faces an acute shortage of cultivable land, which is being met both by intensive use of land available—two crops of sugar cane and rice annually—and by large schemes for land reclamation by drainage and irrigation.

Mining is perhaps even more important for the future. Manganese is being developed, deposits of iron ore, copper and other minerals are being investigated and four licences have been granted in the past year to prospect for oil. A new source of diamonds has trebled production in nine years, but gold production no longer contributes substantially to the economy.

Few students realise that the Kaieteur Falls on the Potaro River has a perpendicular drop more than four times that of Niagara Falls—741 feet, in fact—with enormous HEP potential.

The government must constantly seek new sources of income and employment, for as it says itself, the population is "expanding at a perilous rate", the result largely of successful measures taken to eliminate malaria.

H

HAITI

10,700 sq m. Pop. 4·6m. Because of political troubles per capita income has dropped to £23, lowest in the hemisphere. Ninety per cent of Haiti's people are illiterate.

HOLLAND

13,500 sq m. Pop. 12·2m. Holland is still so prosperous that it has to employ more than 100,000 foreign workers. Exports and imports have reached record levels and the country makes much money through entrepôt trade. It is no exaggeration to say that Holland is now the entrepôt *country* of Europe, especially as Europort develops. Great benefits will accrue from the extensive methane deposits. Those at Groningen are the second largest so far discovered in the world and are the equivalent of 1,000m tons of coal. By the early 1970s Dutch exports of natural gas are expected to reach 20,000m cubic metres a year. Long-term contracts have been made with Germany and Belgium. Holland is one of the few countries with a "complete" oil industry. It has its own oilfields and Europe's largest refinery (the Royal Dutch Shell installation at Pernis), is a leader in the development of petrochemicals and has the world's ninth largest tanker fleet.

The Polders. The newest polder, Southern Flevoland, which has an area of 100,000 acres, is proceeding to schedule. The 45-mile dyke should be completed in 1967. At Lelystad, the future capital of the southern polders, which will eventually house 30,000 people, the first 1,000 houses are already built. At Dronten, on Eastern Flevoland, a town of 5,000 inhabitants is planned. An average polder farm is 115 acres.

Delta Plan. There is a misconception that part of the idea of the Delta Plan, which extends from Flushing to Rotterdam, is to reclaim land; in fact, very little land will be gained by completion of the barriers across the common delta of the Rhine, Meuse and Scheldt. Besides securing the safety of the existing land—the Plan came into being following the disastrous floods of 1953—the Plan's aims are to fight the salination of the rivers and adjoining channels and so increase agricultural production. But the scheme has other geographical benefits. With the building of the new dykes, the islands of the delta will be taken out of their geographical isolation. This is happening now. Fine new roads run along the top of the dykes, providing a fast link with Rotterdam and relieving some of the congestion on the E10, the great Euroroute highway that enters the Netherlands via Antwerp and proceeds to Rotterdam and beyond. Another advantage of the scheme is that, when the islands are joined together, a series of freshwater lakes will be created. The Dutch see in this the opportunity to create a new natural playground, a country of wooded lakes and sandy beaches that will attract tourists. Some idea of the magnitude of the task can be gauged from this: when the Delta Plan is complete the Haringvliet, the sea "valve" of the Plan, must be able to pass river water into the sea at 6m gallons a second. Begun in 1956, the Plan will not be completed until 1978.

HONDURAS

43,227 sq m. Pop. 2·2m. In this least developed of Central American countries coffee production is decreasing, but cotton production has soared by 60% annually for the last three years: the bulk of the crop goes to Japan. Bananas are increasing and tobacco is being grown in larger quantities. Citrus fruit is being exported in quantity for the first time. Factories to process local produce being built during 1967 include a cotton-seed oil mill, a corn starch factory, a sugar mill, a cotton weaving and spinning mill. Products that will be manufactured during 1967–8 include chemicals, pharmaceuticals, cosmetics, aerosol containers, rubber footwear and plastic household wear. The Development Plan 1965–70 is concentrating on ports and roads. The World Bank and the International Development Organisation have granted Honduras a loan of £3·2m for road-building. Most of the money will be spent on the so-called North Road, which will run from the capital, Tegucigalpa, to the commerical centre of San Pedro Sula and will be an important link between the Pacific and the Atlantic.

HONG KONG

398 sq m. Pop. 3·85m. Space is still the colony's major problem (80% of the population lives in 12 square miles) but it is being met in part by shaving mountains and dumping the debris into the sea. Hong Kong now has about 2,500 acres of totally reclaimed land. Reclamation of land is a tremendous task. One project requires the excavation and dumping of 1·25m cubic yards of rock and 4·75m cubic yards of decomposed rock and the dredging and removal of 1·3m cubic yards of mud and sand. Hong Kong's old reputation as a trading centre has now

been overtaken by its new reputation as an industrial centre. In 1955 factories accounted for less than a quarter of Hong Kong's total exports: the position is now reversed, with domestic industry contributing no less than 77% of total export earnings. Textile manufacture is now the largest industry, employing about 40% of the labour force and providing half the colony's exports. Dependence on textiles has long been recognised as a weakness and many new industries have been set up. Hundreds of plastic articles are made and the transistor radio industry, set up only in 1959, now has 35 factories. Britain and the U.S. are Hong Kong's biggest buyers. Hong Kong's heavy industry is still largely restricted to ships—building, repairing and breaking. Until recently most of the scrap was sent to Japan, but now Hong Kong has its own steel mills, which supply the building industry. Nearly 30% of Hong Kong's exports go to the U.S., but trade with most European countries and with Australia and Canada is showing encouraging improvement.

It is important to appreciate Hong Kong's entrepôt trade. China's direct sales through Hong Kong in 1965 amounted to £150m; this made Hong Kong China's most important source of foreign money. Tourism has now become a significant sector of the Hong Kong economy, with more than 400,000 visitors, apart from "transit travellers", annually.

The government is financing a project to dig a tunnel to link Hong Kong with Kowloon on the mainland: this should bring money to several industries. The mile-long tunnel, carrying four lanes of traffic, is due to be completed in August 1970.

Water supplies are precarious with the population increasing so rapidly and large-scale water storage schemes are in progress. Imported water from China costs £1m annually. By the end of 1967 a full survey of Hong Kong's water resources will be nearly complete. Before 1968 at least three other water supply schemes will be in operation, which is just as well as the demand is increasing by 10% a year. Hong Kong has a scheme to desalt several million gallons of water a day with the heat from its public incinerator.

HUNGER

This is an extremely wide subject and cannot easily be compressed into a short account. Hunger and over-population are the greatest problems in the world today. It is enough to say here that 10,000 people die each day from hunger and that by United Nations estimates over half the people now alive will die before their time from malnutrition. More than half the world's people live with perpetual hunger.

In this, in many ways the most perfect of all centuries, the world is annually short of 60m tons of animal food-products, 50m tons of fruit and vegetables and 5·5m tons of oils and fat needed to feed the human race adequately. The developing nations must increase their production of food by 40% by 1975, of legumes by 100% and of animal foods by 120%.

Hunger also follows any natural disaster. Between 1963 and 1966 the FAO has done much to lessen the blows of such disasters as drought, floods, earthquakes, cyclones and political upheavals—which cause as much damage as any natural disaster. For example, nearly £25m has been committed to 33 cases of emergency in 26 countries.

In October 1966 Dr. R. B. Sen, Director-General of the FAO, stated that the world food situation was more precarious than at any time since the acute shortage immediately after World War II. Food production had dropped for 1966, according to preliminary estimates, by 4% to 5%.

HURRICANES

In 1965 Hurricane Betsy caused nearly £250m worth of damage in the United States. The U.S. also suffered from seven major tornadoes. Hurricanes are annual events in the south-east U.S.

HYDRO-ELECTRIC POWER

The continuous development of HEP is commensurate with that of population, industry and standards of living, and though less publicised is as important as developments in oil and gas. In Britain in October 1965 the major power station inside Ben Cruachan was opened. Throughout Europe between 1964 and 1966 several important plants commenced operations or were in the process of building. They include two in southern Albania and four in Austria—at Zillertal in the Tyrol, at Freistritz, Rosegg and Hollenburg. The important Kiev HEP station on the River Dnieper was completed in November 1964.

Probably the most interesting and significant of all HEP stations is the tidal power station built in a half-mile barrage across the River Rance near St. Malo, France. The tidal filling and emptying of the $8\frac{1}{2}$ sq m. artificial lake behind the barrage drives the 24 double-action turbines. The Soviet Union is already copying the principle with a tidal power station at Kislaya Cuba on the White Sea.

Several HEP projects are in progress in North America. One of the most important to be completed recently (end of 1965) is the 240,000 hp plant at Twin Falls on Unknown River, Labrador. Construction of three Columbia River Treaty projects in British Columbia began late in 1964: the first must be operational in April 1968.

HYDROPONICS

The growing of food without soil is becoming an important industry, though it has received little publicity. It has been established in the U.S., Sweden, Korea, the Republic of South Africa, parts of Arabia and in the Dutch West Indies. Units are mostly large in size. Movable plastic tents on frameworks of light alloy cover concentrated crops of a wide variety of foods on rocky, stony or sandy ground. The plastic allows through 25 per cent more ultra-violet light than glass. The plants grow in vermiculite or in substitute mixtures of sand, gravel and desiccated or granulated kelp, which provide good texture for root growth, and are fed with chemical solutions.

Hydroponics is superior to normal irrigation methods because it uses only the minimum amount of water needed for plant health. Also, hydroponics permits more concentrated planting and high yields. A plot 50 ft by 4 ft could easily yield 800 lb of potatoes or tomatoes. Losses by disease and by pests are practically non-existent. Hydroponic culture is specially suitable for terraced regions in Middle East and Mediterranean countries, but it can be used almost anywhere. By use of hydroponics vast amounts of food can be grown in food-short countries. After the initial outlay the cost of producing food is less than the cost of normal production. One chemist can supervise a large area of hydroponic farm.

I

ICELAND

40,500 sq m. Pop. 189,000. Iceland's satisfactory rate of growth is largely due to fine results from the fishing industry, which dominates the economy. Fish and fish products account for 95% of the country's exports. A larger fleet and use of modern techniques have increased the catch by more than 50% since 1958. However, Icelanders fear that stocks in their traditional fishing areas may diminish. Competition is also serious, especially from Russia, Japan, Chile and Peru. Consequently, Iceland is developing her HEP, which it hopes will attract industry. In fact, this has already happened and now manufactures include cement, clothing, furniture, fertilisers, paints and confectionery. During 1965 West Germany displaced Britain as Iceland's chief supplier and the U.S. will probably also soon be ahead of Britain. Nevertheless, Britain exports a wide range of products to Iceland, which may join EFTA.

ILLITERATES

UNESCO has estimated that there are more than 700m people in the world who cannot read or write, about 20% of the total. Efforts by many countries to improve their education systems have not been able to keep pace with the constant increase in their populations. Even Britain has 2·5m total illiterates, according to a 1966 survey.

IMPERIAL CHEMICAL INDUSTRIES

This major company has built or is building large plants in several countries, to make polythene, blasting explosives, dyes, heavy chemicals. In Australia and New Zealand, scores of chemical products that once had to be imported are now made in quantity by I.C.I. I.C.I. associate companies also meet many of the chemical needs of Africa. To these complex activities there is to be added a new group of chemical plants near Rotterdam, which will supply plastics, petrochemicals and related products to the EEC and EFTA.

INDIA

1·2m sq m. Pop. 490m—increasing by 11m annually. Shortage of cereals is one of the most important basic problems, as supply cannot keep pace with increase in population. Industrial development, too, has failed to expand at the planned rate, although India is determined to increase the output of steel, cement, fertilisers, electric power and petrochemicals. Without continued foreign aid on a massive scale India's future would be even more bleak than it is now. For every five dollars India receives she has to pay out three in interest and repayments on earlier loans.

One large development is the power station near Jog Falls on the River Sharavati, which is only 82 miles long. This station, the largest river power station in southern Asia, will provide power for an industrial area being built up at Bangalore. It will be particularly useful in the machine tool, aircraft-building, electrical, steel and paper industries of Mysore. Also it will make possible more extensive mining of high-grade iron, gold and bauxite in Mysore state. Linganmakki Dam, formed by the barrage, is almost two miles long, and can hold an immense amount of water—159 billion cubic feet.

The government has decided to modernise the port of Bombay and has given the contract for the work to an Indian, a British and a Swedish firm. The project, due for completion in 1969, will cost £7·3m and will be financed by the World Bank.

Western Germany has become one of India's most important partners in industrial co-operation. Out of a total of more than 400 firms jointly set up by Indian and foreign enterprises both in 1964 and again in 1965 more than two-thirds involve German partners.

A drive is on foot to stamp out the rodents and other pests which eat at least 10% of India's grain.

At the end of January 1966 speakers at the Pacific Area Travel Association Conference in Delhi said that tourism could earn India at least £375m a year in foreign exchange. At present only 0·5m foreigners pass through India each year (Hong Kong has 1·3m). Tourism would certainly help to give India the money she badly needs to buy food abroad, but the average income per head is only £25.10. Another trouble is the drift to the cities. For instance, at least 100,000 people from rural areas arrive each year in Delhi, where there are already 600,000 homeless.

INDONESIA

887,000 sq m. Pop. 104m. The economic situation has been chaotic, with political unrest, inflation and lack of foreign investment. The rice harvest for 1965 was successful but rice prices have been under pressure and the commodity is the principal import. This is a serious turnabout, for Indonesia was for many years a rice exporter. Bali, an Indonesian island, has not yet recovered from the eruption in 1963 of the Gunung Agung volcano, which buried two of the island's largest rice-growing areas under volcanic ash. The government is trying to achieve self-sufficiency in food and attempts are being made to make maize and potatoes popular. The sugar industry, once one of the world's largest, is also being revitalised. Industrial progress is slow, but plants are being built to supply fertilisers, cement, rayon, iron and steel, tyres and paper. In 1965 Britain had a £5m surplus in trade with Indonesia.

Perhaps the most interesting development is that Dutch exports to Indonesia (once a Dutch colony) are 50% higher than in 1964 and Indonesian sales to Holland are *700%* higher. Apart from the remarkable improvement in Dutch-Indonesian relations, Indonesia has been lent money by West Germany (£14m, most of it for shipping and building of an iron ore plant); by Japan (£1m for the timber industry); China (£18m for industrial development); Pakistan (£4m in export credit). Pakistan can ill afford to lend this money.

IRAN
(Persia)

628,000 sq m. Pop. 22·8m. Three new oilfields have been brought into production and three others discovered, all welcome to a country which now depends on oil for 85% of its foreign earnings. Today 75% of Iran's workers are in agriculture and 25% in industry but the government hopes to reverse these figures within a decade. To bring about this degree of industrialisation a high proportion of Iran's oil and gas and other assets are mortgaged to the Communist world: Russia, for instance, is lending the £103m to build the steel mill complex at Isfahan, the old capital, that will launch the new phase. Production is planned to start in 1971 with a capacity to reach 1·2m tons in three years. The complex will be linked to iron and coal mines and a nation-wide electricity grid powered by a chain of HEP dams. Russia will get gas pumped from fields at Sarajeh and Gorgan in northern Iran. Japan is to buy oil and gas and will, jointly with Iran, develop petro-chemical and plastics industries. Dutch, Swedish and West German firms are building a new port costing £4m at Bandar Bushehr on the Persian Gulf. It is due for completion in 1967. The World Bank, the U.S. and Hungary have all recently lent Iran large amounts. Czechoslovakian, U.S., British, French, German and Italian motor car interests are planning assembly plants.

Iran has great tourist potential on the Caspian Sea shores which could be to the Middle East and Eastern Europe what the Costa Brava is to Western Europe. This is a very productive area where flourish melons, water-melons, pomegranates, peaches, apricots, cherries, grapes, pears and other fruits.

IRAQ

172,000 sq m. Pop. 7·1m. Oil production has increased rapidly in recent years, reaching 64m tons in 1965. The Five-Year Development Plan 1965–9 aims at an annual growth rate of 8%. Under the plan, dams, irrigation projects and land re-clamation figure largely. At present, by recent survey, only one-third of the cultivable land is actually used. Major con-tracts, such as the Kigkuk Irrigation Scheme and the Hilla Artificial Textile project have been awarded to foreign firms, which need to import skilled labour. A Finnish company has been commissioned to work out plans for the Mossul dam, under an agreement on technical and economic assistance be-tween Finland and Iraq.

IRON ORE

(Mostly discussed under country headings.)

On Baffin Island a strike has been made of an estimated 180m tons of ore with an iron content of 69%—this is the highest iron content in the world. (Most of Britain's iron ore has less than 30% iron: high-grade Swedish and U.S. ore has 50% iron content.)

Something like 1,000m tons of ore has been found in the Donets Basin, Ukraine, and other huge (quantity as yet unassessed) deposits have been located on the Kerch Peninsula, Crimea. An important magnetic iron ore source, with 55% iron content, is to be exploited in the Urals, near Mount Kruglaya. Yet another major deposit, 150m tons, has been uncovered in the Kara-Mazar mountains, north of Tadzhikistan.

In Liberia late in 1965 mining began on ore deposits in the Bong Mountains: annual output will be 3m tons. Three other large ore mines are in operation. In 1965 Liberia produced 15m tons of ore. Even Sudan now has iron ore mines—at Fodikwan, about 160 miles north of Port Sudan.

In 1965 the Wabush Mines iron ore project commenced in the Quebec-Labrador Trough: this is the third major ore operation to have started in the southern part of the Trough since 1961. (See *Australia*.)

IRRIGATION

It would be difficult to over-emphasise the importance of irrigation as a subject of study or as a means of increasing food production and standards of living. It is one of the main methods by which the world's rapidly growing population will be fed. Only a representative selection of newer schemes can be dealt with here.

Aden. The Western Protectorate of Aden has an interesting

co-operative—the Abyan Scheme—developed jointly by the Colonial Development and Welfare Board, a board of tenant farmers, the Western Protectorate States and the government. The Abyan Scheme is based on 120,000 irrigated acres which are producing excellent crops.

Algeria. This country, not usually quoted as having irrigation projects, nevertheless has 16 major schemes eating into its semi-arid areas. The projects range from oasis development to basin irrigation.

Australia. In sugar areas at Ayr, Queensland, and on banana plantations at Carnarvon, W.A., revolutionary measures are being used to replenish underground water beds artificially so that an expanding area of sugar can be irrigated. If successful, the scheme may be applied to other regions where sub-artesian supplies are inadequate. In Queensland the works consist of electrically driven pumps to lift water from the Burdekin River into plantation and sheep station creeks. From here the discharged waters will percolate into the underground beds. By this means it is hoped to make available an average of about 40,000 acre-feet of water a year for recharging of the sub-artesian basin.

Ord River. The Ord River drains a catchment area of 18,000 sq m. and during the summer wet season pours into the sea at 1·6m cubic feet a second. The Ord and other rivers of the Kimberley region, which covers 162,000 sq m., are being harnessed. About 20,000 irrigated acres of the Ord Scheme have already been allotted to farmers and about 200,000 acres will eventually be irrigated. Cotton will be the main crop.

Guyana. The Black Bush Polder Project has brought a further 30,000 acres of land into use for rice cultivation. This area employs 27,000 people. The 35,000-acre Tapakuma project will make further notable differences.

Ceylon. In the east of the country the Gal-Oya Scheme has opened up 25,000 new acres, including one 10,000-acre plantation.

Chile. Rainfall figures at Arica, Chile, on Chile's Atacama coast, have averaged 0·6mm annually. Despite this virtual total aridity, Arica's water supply shows no sign of becoming a limiting factor on the economic development of town and district. From sources 160 feet below the surface, additional wells, pumps, aqueducts and storage tanks have greatly increased the supply. More than 4,000 acres are irrigated in the Azapa Valley inland from Arica, mostly for the production of large, high-grade olives for export to the U.S., as well as oranges, vegetables, dairy cattle and poultry. Another 6,000 acres are to be added.

Egypt. (See main text.)

France. From the lower Rhône almost to the Spanish frontier a vast stretch of sunbaked land is gradually being transformed into a fertile fruit and vegetable garden. Irrigation is the keynote of the scheme, for wherever water exists in a Mediterranean area almost any kind of cultivation can be practised. By 1975, when the project is complete, about 420,000 acres bounded by the Massif Central, the Mediterranean and the Rhône will be under irrigation. Connected with the scheme is a modern marketing complex at Nîmes, at which teleprinters bring in continual reports from Covent Garden, Milan, Brussels, Paris and Hamburg.

Greece. In the Lake Copais Basin is an interesting scheme in which a girdle canal collects the upland water, carries it to a great central canal, which distributes it to the irrigated land. An outlet drain and tunnel carry away the excess. On the Salonika Plain a water control and reclamation scheme based on the Axios and Aliakmon Rivers is proving successful.

India. In the Damodar Valley Project, Bihar, seven dams are the basis of a scheme covering irrigation, navigation, flood control and HEP. The Tungabhadra Scheme has put 2m acres under irrigation—resulting in an increase of about 160,000 tons of food grains and 90,000 tons of cash crops yearly.

Israel. In the Gaya Scheme water has been raised from the subsoil by wells and pumps. This scheme, which supports citrus fruit, is a fine example of irrigation with a sense of urgency, as was the transformation of the Negev Desert into a great fertile farm.

Italy. The Pontine Marshes, the Salerno schemes, works in Sardinia, the Tirso Project, the Flumendosa dam in Sicily—these and other projects irrigate about 1·6m acres—a vast increase since 1945.

Kenya. More than half Kenya's 220,000 sq m. has insufficient rain for normal growth and is semi-arid or desert, but the total potential fresh water irrigation is probably 1m acres. The Tana River Irrigation Project is the most encouraging and largest plan to date. On the Mwea-Tebere Irrigation Scheme on the Upper Tana the government hopes to have 12,000 acres under crops by 1970. Already the area produces 12,000 tons of rice. Pilot schemes are under way on the Lower Tana, but the FAO survey being made of the 600,000 acres here will not be complete until 1967. Other schemes are possible with water from springs from the foot of Mt. Kilimanjaro.

Lebanon. The Kasmieh scheme, which uses irrigation tunnels and incorporates the River Orontes, north of Homs, is built on a dam dating back to Roman times. Private irrigation is practised on the narrow coastal strip between the hills and the Mediterranean—grain, bananas, oranges and grapes are grown. Owners here often form little syndicates to keep in good order the irrigation channels and to distribute water.

Morocco. Between 1921 and 1966 the population grew from $3\frac{1}{2}$ million to $13\frac{1}{2}$ million. This helps to account for the development of irrigation, especially the Kasba Tadla Scheme and the Bin-el-Widan Scheme.

Mozambique. A barrage on the Limpopo River has made possible the remarkably successful Limpopo Valley and Settlement Scheme. This was a difficult project for various reasons and is a prime example of how obstacles may be overcome. Unlike other African countries, the Portuguese Overseas Provinces receive no international aid and so the entire 74,000 acres had to be irrigated by local or Portuguese resources. The fascination of the scheme, as of others in Portuguese Africa, is that in a continent so divided by racial laws or attitudes, and by racial fears, settlement here is open to all with the requisite skills and culture, so that Africans and Europeans are intermingled and share the same facilities. The Limpopo Scheme should be studied by any country or organisation facing irrigational problems of any kind. Here the Portuguese and Africans appear to have conquered all of them, and cannot be too highly praised.

Nigeria. This country has an interesting scheme on the Niger, comparable in some ways to the Nile schemes. The Samsanding Project has brought 700,000 acres under irrigation.

Peru. There has long been small-scale irrigation in Peru, but in 1959 a project was begun to add 500,000 acres to the 4,477,000 then under cultivation. The coastal plain and western slopes areas concerned are already producing cotton, sugar, vegetables and grapes. The World Bank has granted Peru £4m for the San Lorenz project, which is to assist the irrigation and settlement of a total of 123,500 acres of infertile land along the Peruvian coast.

Qâttara (Kattara) Project. In 1960 German industrial engineers, the company of Siemens in particular, proposed to dig a canal to connect the Mediterranean Sea with the Qâttara Basin—perhaps better known in Britain as the Qâttara Depression. The resulting flow of water would irrigate the desert and generate electricity. Completion of the plan, could, according to the planners, change the climate of the Libyan Desert by causing convectional cloud formation. The idea is still being pursued and Siemens have received credit offers from many parts of the world. It seems very likely that before long the scheme will be started.

Rhodesia. The Lowveld Schemes. By early 1964 the Triangle Estates and the Hippo Valley Estates had between them more than 30,000 acres planted to sugar-cane. Expansion is taking place on both estates and by 1967 their combined sugar plantings should reach 55,000 acres. Even more sugar is to be planted. A new company, Nandi Sugar Estates, has been formed to grow sugar a few miles north of Hippo Valley and will have 15,000 acres under cane by 1967. Water from the project will come from the Manjirenji Dam on the Chiredzi

River. Increase in sugar output has changed Rhodesia from an importer to an exporter of sugar.

Russia. A dam is being built across the Amu Darya near the town of Takhia-Tash, 10 miles south of Nukus, on the railway from Urgench. When completed the river will irrigate—according to Russian figures—2·5m acres of desert land, including the River Atrek valley in western Turkmenia. The figure, though large, is possible: several other Russian irrigation schemes have been executed on a massive scale. Throughout the Soviet Union at least 16 irrigation projects are in various stages of completion, mostly along the very long southern part of the Union.

Spain. Spain is rightly proud of its sprawling Plan Badajoz, the 100-mile-long irrigation project along the Guadiana River near the Portuguese border. Here a former malarial swamp has been turned into fertile fields that make Spain all but self-sufficient in cotton and rice.

Sudan. The Gezira Scheme is a good example of a government-controlled scheme. About 30,000 tenants have been settled here, each with a 40-acre holding on which a stipulated crop must be grown. The first stage of the Roseires Irrigation Project was completed in 1966 when the dam across the Blue Nile was finished. Eventually something like 1m acres of land will be brought into use.

Tanzania. The Myumba Ya Munga Dam on the Pangani River will bring into use 56,000 acres of agricultural land in the Pangani Valley.

Zambia. The plain around the Kafue River, being alluvial, was long regarded as potentially fertile but it needed water. As the result of a visionary scheme and with intensive dyke irrigation the area is remarkably productive.

Interesting schemes also exist in Thailand, Madagascar, Mexico, Nicaragua, Turkey, among other countries. Great developments are likely in the USSR—from the Volga and other southern rivers which command a very large potential area—in India, in French West Africa, Egypt and the Sudan, and in North America and Brazil.

ISRAEL

7,992 sq m. Pop. 2·5m. The extraordinary vitality of this country continues, despite continuous Arab hostility. It is most evident in the further settlement of the Negev Desert, much of which is no longer desert but an area of flourishing orchards and farms. Beersheba, in the northern Negev, has changed from a village to a large town; Eilat, the once waterless outpost on the Red Sea, is now an important port handling something approaching 400,000 tons of cargo annually. Near the Dead Sea is the new concrete town of Arad which has sprung up out of the desert and at Ashdod, south of Tel Aviv, the Israelis are building a great new trading port that will ultimately have 150,000 inhabitants. In the Galilean hills is yet another new industrial city—Carmiel. Citrus plantations in western Israel are expanding fast, and the potash, copper sulphate, phosphates, bromide and salt industries are progressing. Israel has so far found only small quantities of oil—they supply about 10% of the country's needs—but fields in the Negev are being explored. Tourism is bringing in more money than ever before, largely because Israel now has cruise ships of her own. Immigrants are entering the country at a rate of 65,000 annually. Israel's main trading partners are the U.S., Britain and, to an increasing extent, Japan. The country's main development problem is its dependence on foreign capital, especially from the U.S., but the growth rate, 10% in 1965, is some compensation. The Common Market's fixing, in 1966, of minimum prices for Israel oranges—the main foreign exchange earner—was almost a calamity. Citrus exports now amount to about 15m crates, an increase of nearly 4m crates on the 1963–4 shipments.

ITALY

131,000 sq m. (including Sicily and Sardinia). Pop. 52·6m.
Italy, recovering slowly from a recession in 1964, has been
helped by the iron and steel and motor car industries. With new
plant coming into use, steel production has risen sharply:
figures for 1965, for instance, were 30% up on those for 1964.
Early in 1965 there was a merger between Montecatini, the
huge chemical-minerals complex, and the Edison Group, a
private power company that switched to heavy industry in
order to survive when Italy nationalised power in 1962. The
resulting company has replaced Fiat as Italy's biggest business,
and it is to build six chemical plants for Russia.

The most interesting new aspect of Italian geography is the
complex and ambitious attempt to improve the area south of
Rome. The main targets for improvement are Taranto, which
now has a large steel complex, Latina (near Naples) where
there is a trading estate, methane at Ferrandina and petrochemical complexes in eastern Sicily, notably at Syracuse.
Much is being done, too, to improve agriculture. The rivers of
southern Italy dry up in summer, so one plan is to trap winter
rains in subterranean storage tanks and use the water for summer irrigation. The drift of population to the north is not so
marked as it was up to the end of 1964, but new northern
industries, especially around Mestre (near Venice) are still
attracting poorer southerners.

In June 1965 the World Bank lent Italy £100m to help
finance industrial development in the south. It seems clear
that, with the obvious success of expansion in the south, further
capital will not be difficult to raise. Already, several large
American companies are planning to build factories in
southern Italy.

It is not generally known that Valdagno, a village in
northern Italy, now has Europe's largest spinning and weaving
plant. It is part of the industrial empire of the Marzotto family,
who own textile plants in six other Italian towns and are

Europe's largest producers of woollen goods. Despite automation one mill alone has 8,000 workers.

During 1965 the Italian Shipping Line, which is state-owned, introduced two luxury liners, an unprecedented step in a single year. They are the twin ships *Michelangelo* and *Raffaello*, 45,900 tons. The Italian government believes that the ships will bring tens of thousands of tourists to Italy and 70% of them will be Americans. Tourism remains Italy's main source of foreign exchange—about £450m a year.

A Milan geologist warned in 1966 of what he calls the "alarming" sinking of the ground in the low-lying Po River valley and particularly in the delta. He calculates that the ground in the delta region is subsiding at the rate of 7–10 inches annually. This is much more than the 1·7 to 3 centimetres annual subsidence reported in Venice. Extreme subsidence could be serious at time of flood. The valley of the 405-mile Po is Italy's most extensive and fertile plain and through much of it the land lies below the level of the river, from which it is protected by embankments. It seems possible that the whole north-west coast of the Adriatic is subject to a general sinking, largely explained by the geological youth of the region around the Po delta.

IVORY COAST

124,000 sq m. Pop. 3·75m. This republic is Black Africa's most flourishing young colony and is now the third largest coffee producer and fourth largest for cocoa. Aware of the dangers of a two-crop economy, Ivory Coast is developing soyabeans, peanuts, pineapples and palm oil.

During 1966 a West German firm cleared 50,000 acres of jungle for new plantations. Per capita income for Ivorians is the highest in Black Africa—about £100 a year.

J

JAMAICA

4,411 sq m. Pop. 1·7m. To ensure that every productive piece of land is brought into use the government has introduced the Land Utilization Act (1965) which permits compulsory government purchase of land if the private owner does not develop it. Entirely new village communities will be created on acquired land. Strenuous efforts are being made to revitalise Jamaican agriculture by improving farming techniques, disease control, plant breeding and marketing. Jamaica now has more than 19,000 sugar-cane farmers and sugar cane, rum and molasses account for about a third of the country's visible exports. Because of the Commonwealth Sugar Agreement, Jamaica (and other West Indian islands) can sell sugar to Britain at £47 a ton at a time when the depressed world price is £21 a ton. The agreement runs to the end of 1973.

Tourism has increased so much that, with an income of £23m in 1965, it is second only to bauxite as Jamaica's chief money-earning industry. Most ambitious of Jamaica's tourism projects is to restore the town of Port Royal, the infamous pirate sanctuary in the seventeenth century. Jamaica is now the world's largest producer of bauxite, much of it in the form of alumina. The entire output is sent to Scandinavia and Canada.

JAPAN

182,700 sq m. Pop. 98·5m. A country of such industrial and agricultural vitality and diversity is bound to have ups and downs and Japan had a recession early in 1965, with a consequent falling-off of domestic trade. However, exports have increased and there can be no doubt that Japan's future prosperity is assured. It would be waste of space to comment further on Japan's pre-eminent position as a ship-building nation, though it must be said that the country is still improving its techniques and, producing 45% of the world's tonnage, appears to be in an unassailable position.

The three aspects of Japan's new geography which demand most attention are:

1. The attempt to decentralise industry
2. Plans to improve agricultural productivity still further.
3. The extraordinary growth of Japanese-Australian trade.

The need for spreading industry can be clearly seen by the fact that the seaboard between Tokio and Osaka contains only 16% of Japan's land, yet it holds 43% of the population and half the 500,000 factories. The lone highway between the two cities is often hopelessly traffic-jammed. This was partly why the railway service was improved so drastically, so that now 60 passenger trains a day make the 320-mile run in four hours a trip. The line, incidentally, included the building of 548 bridges, 66 tunnels and 57 miles of embankment. The Tokaido Line serves all of Japan's six largest cities, but is of particular importance to Osaka (pop. 5·5m) the centre of Japan's commerce. With adjoining Kobe, Osaka ships 42% of Japan's exports and is a ship-building centre. Its factories have diversified from traditional cotton spinning into electronics, chemicals, and precision machinery.

Efforts to bring about industrial decentralisation are based on efforts to induce industrialists and workers to live in Hokkaido, especially in the cities of Hakodate and Sapporo, at Fukui in west Honshu and in areas of southern Kyushu and southern Shikoku. After nearly 100 years of emigration to Hokkaido the population of the island is still no more than 5m —a mere 5% of all Japanese. The government hopes that the tunnel being built between Honshu and Hokkaido, across Tsugaru Strait, will encourage emigration, if only because the greater ease of transport will interest industrialists in setting up businesses in Hokkaido. The possibility of industrialisation in the other chosen areas seems brighter.

Agriculturally, Japan is the most productive of all Asian countries, but it is trying to become even more self-sufficient. Japanese agricultural diversity and productivity are object lessons to the world.* Six-sevenths of Japan's total area cannot be cultivated and though there are about 4,000 Japanese to each square mile of arable land—easily the highest proportion in the world—Japan now imports less than a quarter of its food supplies. No scrap of land is ignored—that around the base of telegraph posts, triangles formed by the convergence of roads, all are planted. The Japanese have done away with all fences and the small foot-wide banks of earth separating the fields are planted with vegetables, usually beans or peas. Farms are small, averaging only $2\frac{1}{2}$ acres (the average English farm is 100 acres) and the work is very hard but the Japanese farmer does have something to sell, the heavy urban concentrations of industrial workers have the money to pay, and consequently the Japanese farmer can buy fertiliser to increase the quality of his fields, already fertile from improved water control (no erosion losses), silt brought in by water, and long use of excreta and compost.

By skilled crop rotation and careful manuring the Japanese farmer is now growing two crops in the same field in the same year; often the second crop is sown before the first has been harvested. Barley and wheat, for instance, are usually planted in drills and a few months before the grain crop ripens the farmer will sow a crop like tomatoes between the drills. The grain crop is cut by hand to avoid injury to the tomato

* Not all of what follows is, strictly speaking, new, but it has had little mention in print.

seedlings. When the barley or wheat has been lifted the drills are split and the tomatoes are off to a flying start.

Small, compact and highly efficient threshing and winnowing machines and ploughs have become commonplace in Japan. As there is now scarcely a place in Japan without electricity the farmers use power for many purposes, including farm machines.

One FAO officer, Dr. Hambridge, has said that if Japanese-type intensive agriculture were practised in east and south-east Asia the result would be a fantastic surplus production of food and a resulting increase in the standard of living.

Japan's trade with Australia is growing so rapidly that almost every week there is news of a further agreement. In the last two years Japan has agreed to buy huge quantities of Australian iron ore from five different fields. One order is for £400m worth of ore. In addition, Japan is to buy coal worth £125m from a Queensland mine at Moura. Yawata Steel Company claims that this will be the biggest and longest term coal import deal (13 years) to be concluded by Japan with a single coal mine.

On top of all this, Japan has signed a 10-year agreement for 1m tons of bauxite a year, to be mined on Cape York. Apart from traditional imports from Australia, such as wool, Japan is also buying much sugar, zinc, copper and food.

In various deals similar to those with Australia Japan has ensured vast quantities of raw materials for years to come. Japan has arranged to provide Russia with £70m worth of pipe and liquefaction equipment with which to develop the Okha methane fields in Sakhalin Island. In return Japan will get 7m cubic feet of gas yearly. Japanese oil interests have promised to invest £5m in oil drilling in the sea off Sumatra (Indonesia) and will take 61% of the oil obtained. The Mitsui Mining and Smelting Company has bought copper and zinc mines in Peru and from 1967 will import large quantities of concentrated ores. Other copper is being imported from Canada, the Philippines, Bolivia and South Africa (Transvaal).

Japanese interests own a pulp mill at Sitka, Alaska, which

from a lease of 1·5m acres of forest, ships back to Japan 165,000 tons of pulp annually; that is, 85% of Japan's pulp imports. Similarly, Japan is exploiting other sources in Borneo and Canada. Japan has invested £7m to develop iron ore resources in India and will get further ore from Goa and Brazil.

Japan depends on imports for 99% of its oil and is a partner in ventures with Kuwait and Saudi Arabia: in 1966 it received 68m barrels from the tri-nation Arabian Oil Co., which is operating in offshore Kuwait.

In 1965 Japan's imported raw materials amounted to 205m tons, a 20% increase on the 1964 figures. It is likely that future increases will average up to 25% annually.

JORDAN

34,750 sq m. Pop. 1·9m. In April 1963 torrential rain flooded Siq Gorge at Petra and drowned a guide, a French priest and 21 young Frenchwomen tourists. Anxious to keep tourists visiting Jordan, the authorities have reconstituted a 2000-year-old dam on the Siq. The dam was not designed to prevent an entire flood, merely to check its water and divert it into a system of guide walls and a tunnel a quarter of a mile long. The water is finally discharged into two wadis where it can do no damage. Apart from the dam and diversion system, Petra has a spreading network of channels cut into the rock to lead water to the city from distant springs. The entire system is to be put into use again. Agricultural development depends on some ambitious irrigation plans. Late in May 1966 work started on the Mukhaiba Dam, part of an Arab scheme to use the River Jordan and its tributaries to counter Israeli plans to divert the river. Jordan is now producing salt in the Jordan Valley.

JUTE

The long-range outlook is poor, because this raw material is struggling against increasing competition from synthetic substitutes.

In 1965 world production was 3·2m metric tons, with India and Pakistan each producing more than 1m tons. India may soon displace Pakistan as the largest producer. The only other growers of any importance are the Republic of China, Thailand, Brazil, Congo, Burma and Formosa. Despite the few growers, it is important to note that Pakistan no longer dominates the market.

K

KOREA (South)

37,436 sq m. Pop. 28·3m. Korea's Five-Year Economic Plan ended in 1966 and so it is useful to study its effects. Agricultural production has risen, largely because of better use of pesticides: the fishing and forestry industries have also been more productive. Industrial output has declined, except in spinning and weaving. Growth is largely dependent on grants from the U.S. Agency for International Development. The AID has given £4·6m for construction of a thermal power plant at Kunsan. West Germany has financed the building of a pulp factory and a fertiliser factory and has lent £17m for other industries. France has lent £3m for an HEP plant. About half South Korean imports are now from the U.S., its other major trading partners being Japan, West Germany and Italy.

Korean-Japanese relations have improved so much that American domination of the Korean market has been reduced while the Japanese share has risen sharply. Japan will lend Korea £285m under various long-term agreements.

KUWAIT

6,000 sq m. Pop. 468,000. Income from oil has given Kuwait one of the highest living standards of the world and because of it the population has increased by 46% since 1961, with job-seeking immigrants flooding the country. One in every six people is a government employee. Since 1965 Kuwait has reduced its investments in Britain by 50%, to about £185m. A survey has show that Kuwait has enough oil for another 80–100 years: by 1970 annual production is expected to reach 150m tons. On the advice of a World Bank mission, the country is concentrating on the petrochemical industry and a £12·5m fertiliser factory is being built. The present main industry (apart from oil) is food-processing. Foods such as rice, meat and fruit are imported in bulk and prepared and packed for re-export to surrounding countries. By mid-1966 Kuwait had given or lent about £400m to other Arab states.

L

LAKES

Lake Erie. This important lake is now so polluted that it is a major problem in North America. The main reason is that most of the larger tributaries have turned into little more than open sewers. Detroit alone pours 1·5 billion gallons of waste a day into the Detroit River, which flows into Erie. Much of the lake is now a "dead" sea, incapable of supporting any fish life. The programme recently introduced to solve the problem is so complex it cannot have an effect before 1969 and may cost each of the American states affected—Michigan, New York, Indiana, Ohio and Pennsylvania—a billion dollars. It is based on purification of waste before it is discharged into the rivers which flow into Erie. Pollution is more serious in this lake than in the other Great Lakes because of denser settlement and industry around it.

LAOS

90,000 sq m. Pop. 2·6m. Business has been booming, food production has been boosted, plans have been approved for an ambitious HEP project. Some highways have been resurfaced and villages modernised, but the country is almost entirely dependent on U.S. grants.

LEAD

In October 1965, Eire opened its first new mine for 100 years—
at Tynagh, Co. Galway. It is expected to yield 150,000 tons a
year of lead and zinc. In 1967 Bulgaria will mine lead and zinc,
1·2m tons annually, at Kyustendil, in the Osogovo Mountains.

LEBANON

4,300 sq m. Pop. 2·2m. There was a time when Lebanon's
economy was based almost entirely on agriculture and, indeed,
38% of the country's working population are engaged on main
products such as citrus fruits, grain, apples, bananas, figs,
olives and tobacco. But Lebanon now depends for its wealth
mainly on providing financial and commercial services. The
capital, Beirut, has become the commercial and financial capital of the Middle East and has much entrepôt trade. In the last
10 years Beirut's banking business has expanded by more than
1000%. Well over half of Beirut's £500m in deposits comes
from abroad, partly because of extremely strict security laws
which, like those of Switzerland, protect the depositor.

Three of the pipelines from Saudi Arabia and Iraq end at the
ports of Saida, Tripoli and Bamias and 53m tons of oil are
pumped into tankers each year, bringing Lebanon a lot of
money in royalties. Receipts from tourism are rising rapidly:
more than 600,000 people visited the country in 1965. The
country's main hopes for economic and agricultural progress
depend largely on the Litani River irrigation and HEP project.

LIBERIA

43,000 sq m. Pop. 1·32m. It was not until 1951 that iron ore mining began in Liberia. Now there are numerous mines. The fourth largest, operated by a syndicate which includes West German steel firms, commenced operations in 1966. Liberia is now one of Germany's major sources of iron ore. Altogether, Liberia exports about 20m tons of high-grade ore annually.

LIBYA

680,000 sq m. Pop. 1·6m. Libya has some interesting fresh geographical facets, largely resulting from her new oil wealth. The country is now probably the world's eighth largest producer. The government is finding it difficult to spend its oil revenues in a productive way, because these revenues, while improving the standard of living, are also damaging the country as a whole. To explain this paradox: agriculture, which has traditionally provided the main source of employment, is rapidly losing labour as Libyans move to the towns or to the oilfields, where wages are so much higher. Labour is scarce in any case. The government is financing irrigation projects and is providing equipment, fertilisers and insecticides at half cost to farmers, but even this is not arresting the drift from the farms. New industries have been started, such as manufacture of soap, detergents, iron rods, bottles and wrapping paper. By the end of 1966 a £1½m cement kiln will be in operation near Homs. A sugar refinery costing £2½m is in production in Azizia. Main suppliers to Libya are the U.S., Italy, Britain and West Germany.

Interestingly, parts of the Libyan Desert are being stabilised by use of oil and eucalyptus trees are being successfully grown in these areas. The oil dune-treatment helps to conserve the moisture available. About 600,000 acres of dunes in Tripolitania alone are suitable for conversion into productive forest land. There is a scheme to reclaim land from salt flats around Benghazi.

The decision to make Baida the administrative capital of the kingdom seems to be a mistake. Baida is more than three hours by car from Benghazi in an area that is neither attractive nor useful.

Security is a major problem for the Libyans, as their oil installations are desperately vulnerable to sabotage. They are worried about how to guard the new £25m B.P. pipeline running parallel with the Egyptian frontier, with its outlet at Tobruk.

In August 1966 a group of Italian companies won a contract to broaden 1,483 miles of coastal highway and build 46 bridges.

M

MALAWI
(Nyasaland)

45,747 sq m. Pop. 3·9m. Secondary industries have been developing and there are now factories assembling motor cycles and making soap, cigarettes, bricks and cement. Tea, the main industry (20m lb annually), accounts for 40% of the country's agricultural exports.

MALAYSIA

128,703 sq m. Pop. 9m. (Malaya, 7·8m., Sabah (British North Borneo) and Sarawak 1·2m.) The Federation was badly hit in August 1965 when Singapore seceded, and it is possible that it will disintegrate. As is well known, Malaysia depends heavily on rubber and tin, which account for more than 40% and 20% respectively of its export money. The average yield of rubber rises yearly, but synthetic rubber forms an increasing proportion of world trade—75% in the U.S. Malaysia's share of tin production was 41% in 1965. Malaysia's prosperity depends on agricultural and industrial diversification. Fruit canning—of pineapples, especially—is proving successful and the timber trade in Sabah and Sarawak is increasing. Many drainage and irrigation projects are in progress, partly to allow palm oil and sugar-cane planting on a large scale.

139

MALDIVE ISLANDS

Chain of 2,000 coral atolls, covering 115 sq m., of which 200 are inhabited. Pop. 95,000. In July 1955 the Maldives became independent from Britain. Almost all trade is with Ceylon. In return for their fish, copra and tortoise-shell the Maldivians buy rice, sugar, cotton and fuel oils.

MALI

582,437 sq m. Pop. 4·4m. Arid and landlocked, Mali is much more prosperous following help from several nations. France is buying the peanut crop; West Germany has advanced credit for purchase of 300 trucks; the U.S. has given cement and petrol worth 2·5m dollars; the Common Market £1m for irrigation; China has bartered machinery for handicrafts and Russia has offered £15m in long-term credits.

MALTA

122 sq m. Pop. 330,000. The ship-repair yard and building work—long Malta's chief industries—have already been augmented by over 35 new factories built since 1963 and producing a wide range of goods including synthetic fibres, paint, detergents, textiles, spring mattresses, plastics and furniture. Car assembly and light engineering works as well as the export of cut flowers are providing new sources of employment. Further industries are being attracted by special terms e.g. 10 years free of income tax, ready-built factories at nominal rents, freedom from customs duties. Tourism is increasing.

MAURITIUS

805 sq m. Pop. 800,000. The country's main problem is over-population: the population explosion is almost visible. Already there are more than 1,000 Mauritians per acre living off the produce of a third of an acre. The safety line in population is 600,000, but the population is already 800,000. Attempts are being made to set up industries—at present sugar dominates the economy to the extent of 94%—but many Mauritians can never hope for a job.

METHANE

More commonly known as natural gas, methane has become big business. Large quantities are now reaching Britain from North Africa, brought by the *Methane Princess* and the *Methane Progress*: they carry 12,200 tons each trip. The methane is stored on Canvey Island, Thames Estuary, from where it is pumped by pipeline to stations as far away as Coventry, Sheffield and Leeds. Similarly, much Libyan methane will reach Italy and Spain in late 1966. Methane in the North Sea fields is steadily being developed. (See *Britain*.) Much is already being used industrially and domestically in Holland and north Germany and it is only a matter of time before large quantities are used in Britain.

The area of the north Holland (Groningen) field is estimated to be about 100 sq m. The Groningen gas has a calorific value equal to twice that of coal gas and it does not have the sulphur content of Saharan gas and is therefore more valuable. Methane has been found also in Noordholland, near Alkmaar, in Friesland and on the island of Ameland. West Germany is exploiting methane found near Oldenburg, Lower Saxony.

Afghanistan will export gas from its Shibarghan fields in

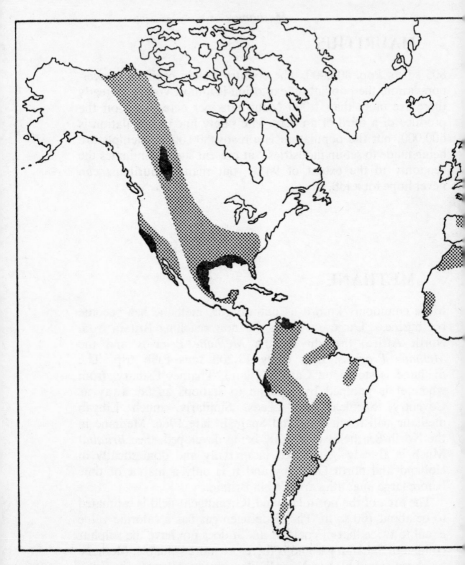

Natural Gas Found 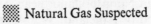 **Natural Gas Suspected**

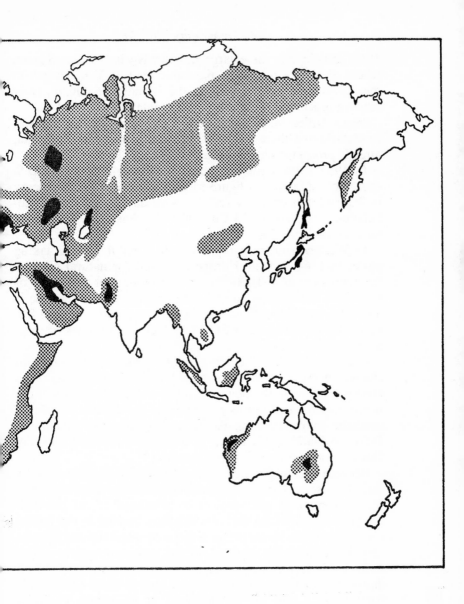

1967. Russia has three large new fields—in western Siberia, where there is a reserve of 6m cubic feet; at Yangikazgan in the Kyzyl-Kum desert, and on the island of Sakhalin, from which a pipeline is being laid to the mainland.

Wells drilled into Lake Erie are providing gas for industry in Ontario and there has been yet another strike in California, already prosperous in methane.

In 1965 natural gas accounted for about 30% of all U.S. energy consumption, a figure roughly equivalent to the energy in 7·5m barrels of heavy fuel oil every day of the year (a calculation by Standard Oil Co.). The U.S. has 260,000 miles of long distance pipeline.

In Western Europe a rapid switch to natural gas is taking place. In 1964 Western Europe's demand for natural gas was the equivalent of 300,000 barrels of oil a day, or about 2% of the area's total energy supply. The average annual increase is now 20% and this rate is expected to continue for at least five years. By mid-1966 the EEC alone had 25,000 miles of long-distance gas pipeline.

Heavy industries, including public utilities, are eager to change to methane for its easy use and calorific value. New chemical plants in the Benelux and West German area will use it not only for fuel but as raw material for various chemicals, synthetic fibres, rubbers, paints and insecticides. In autumn 1966 the Dutch fields began to supply the Thyssen Gas Co, Duisburg with 4m cubic metres yearly.

Because the reserves of gas in the Po Valley are steadily dwindling some is being imported from Libya. The Esso LNG (liquefied natural gas) project is scheduled to go into full operation towards the end of 1968. Gas tankers in the Italian run will go from Marsa el Brega to La Spezia. Over the life of a 25-year contract the amount of gas delivered will be about 235m cubic feet a day (the equivalent of 55,000 barrels of oil daily). Under the same project and also in 1968 110m cubic feet of gas a day will be delivered at Barcelona. Facilities costing £7m are being built in the city.

Large new strikes were made in Australia during 1965 and

1966. The biggest flow is in the Amadeus Basin, 120 miles south-west of Alice Springs, with 40m cubic feet a day. Off the coast of eastern Victoria, at Australia's first offshore well, gas has flowed at the rate of 10·5m cubic feet a day. In Western Australia major strikes have been made at Yardarino, near Geraldton; at Gingin, 55 miles north of Perth, and on Barrow Island, 50 miles off the north-west coast near Onslow. This gas is likely to be used in the development of local iron ore deposits.

MEXICO

758,000 sq m. Pop. 40·1m. Mexico is, and will remain, one of the most rapidly expanding countries in Latin America, with its prosperity geared to mineral wealth—silver, sulphur, lead, zinc, iron ore, manganese and copper. Since 1960 industrial output has increased by 60%, with the emphasis now on heavy industry. In many lines, particularly in consumer goods, Mexico is self-sufficient. Even in agriculture great progress has been made, with an increasingly wide range of crops. The most important for export are sugar, coffee and cotton.

Despite a population increase of 3% yearly Mexico has become virtually self-sufficient in foodstuffs.

Forestry and fisheries are being boosted. Mexico is earning a lot with its thriving tourist trade—£267m in 1965. The U.S. dominates trade with Mexico, but Britain usually has an annual credit balance of about £10m. Under an ambitious plan, entire farm communities are being moved from drier, unproductive regions to Mexico's humid, less populated areas, for example to Campeche state near the Guatemalan border.

That Mexico's economy is healthy is shown by the money lent by various organisations, the World Bank: £48m for agriculture and power, £20m from the Inter-American Development Bank to help finance the building of 5,000 miles of roads.

MILK

Rising production of milk in Britain is a major agricultural problem. As has been pointed out, the British cannot hope to consume an extra 400m gallons by 1970. The difficulty has come about with the increase in herds, a necessary increase, since by 1970 British demand for beef will be for at least £30m worth of beef more than in 1966. The surplus milk is not turned into butter because of long-term contracts to buy foreign butter.

MONETARY REFORM

Throughout 1965 and 1966 the world's big powers tried to improve world finance so that world prosperity would not be damaged by lack of money available to finance world trade. Sharp rises in gold hoarding, as happened late in 1965, are dangerous. At that time the free world's official stores of gold fell by many millions, the first such drop in 10 years. The missing gold had flowed into the hands of rich speculators in industrial countries, such as France and Switzerland. This would lead to a rise in the price of gold, which puts pressure on Europeans as well as on the U.S. Treasury. In the long run, the expansion of world trade requires growth, not shrinkage of monetary reserves. European countries have been reluctant to embark on reforms, contending that the U.S. and Britain must first put their balance of payments in order. Both countries have done so to a large extent. It is hoped that the so-called Group of Ten—Belgium, Britain, Canada, France, Germany, Italy, Japan, Holland, Sweden and the U.S.—will now work towards an agreement on a new international currency to supplement dollars, pounds and gold in world trade.

MONGOLIAN PEOPLE'S REPUBLIC

(Outer Mongolia, not Inner Mongolia, which is still a Chinese province.)

604,000 sq m. Pop. About 1m. Often called "the least known country in the world", Mongolia is nevertheless joining in the general march of progress. The country's iron, coal, tungsten and gold deposits are being exploited and although Ulan Bator, the capital (225,000 inhabitants), is the only major industrial centre there are ambitious hopes for Darkhan, a city nearing completion on the Soviet border. The "railway of the three nations", completed in 1955, which links Ulan Bator with Irkutsk (Russia) and with Peking, is playing a major part in development of the country.

MOON

The Russian success in soft-landing a spacecraft on the moon, achieved with *Luna 9*, in February 1966, was a notable event in geography and was certainly a turning point in space exploration. However, a noted American astronomer, Dr Thomas Gold of Cornell University, said in May that he doubted if the moon's surface could withstand the weight of the American *Lem* (Lunar Excursion Module) scheduled to settle on the moon by 1970. Lem is to weigh 32,000 lb, and will have 4,316 sq inches of landing gear—120 oz to the sq. inch *Luna 9* weighed only 220 lb. The American moon shot in June 1966, achieved by the Surveyor, will perhaps prove to have been more useful than *Luna 9* since the photographs that were received from it appeared to indicate that the moon's surface is not too soft for a landing, but able to support much more than the 2 oz per sq. in. that Dr Gold has calculated. *Surveyor* took 63 hours to cover the 247,000 miles of its flight. Between September 13 1959 and June 2 1966 no fewer than 10 "moon strikes" had been achieved.

MOROCCO

180,000 sq m. Pop. 13·5m (more than half under 20 and 75% rural). Many industries have recently been nationalised, including the export trade in citrus fruit, fresh vegetables, fish products and handicraft goods. Early in 1965 a Three-Year Plan was introduced, replacing an unrealistic Five-Year Plan which had to be abandoned. Agriculture and tourism are the main targets, but money is to be spent on ports, power and communications. However, mining is the economic mainstay and Morocco is the world's largest producer and exporter of phosphates (for fertilisers). Under the Three-Year Plan, production is expected to reach 16m tons by 1970. Mining has been greatly aided by two enormous bucket-wheel excavators provided by West Germany in 1966. With their capacity of 52,970 cubic feet per hour they will help Morocco maintain its position. In June 1965 an £18m chemical complex was opened near Safi, while there is a large sugar-beet factory near Sidi-Slimane. New irrigation schemes are in progress, but can have no positive effect for several years. Main suppliers to Morocco are the U.S., West Germany, Cuba, Holland and Britain.

N

NAURU

This tiny island (less than 1 sq m.) 1,500 miles north-east of Australia, which administers it, is not likely within 30 years to run out of the phosphates on which its existence depends, but plans are already well developed to find a new settlement for the 4,900 Nauruans. The choice of sites seems to have been narrowed down to Curtis and Fraser islands off the Queensland coast.

NEW ZEALAND

104,000 sq m. Pop. 2.6m. Wool, meat, butter and cheese account, usually, for over 80% of New Zealand's total export earnings. This is why the government has embarked on ambitious schemes to diversify industry and to expand markets. For instance in 1956 more than 90% of New Zealand's meat exports went to Britain: the figure is now less than 60%, but about three-quarters of the country's dairy produce still goes to Britain. The government has approved the creation of a native steel industry that will refine ore from New Zealand's black sand beaches. The steel mills at Raglan, west of Hamilton, will cost £52m, but will save, when completed in 1968, nearly £20m annually in imported steel from Britain and Australia. The steel complex will use low-cost power from another new project, a grid of power plants that will generate power from boiling springs and steam and a water race that runs underground for six miles through the rocky soil of South Island. Altogether there are eight schemes, to come into service between 1968 and 1972, which will provide new power from water and geo-thermal resources. One scheme, the Manapouri Project, may be linked with an aluminium industry. There are also plans for nuclear generation. The first major oil refinery, at Whangarei, costing £10m, is designed to serve 90% of the domestic market until 1967, when further expansion will be considered. It is likely that another refinery will be built. Forestry is fast becoming one of New Zealand's major industries, following a massive afforestation programme. The pulp and paper, wood products and plastics industries are expanding rapidly. Over the past 10 years manufacturing output has increased by two-thirds, farming by 37% and construction industries by 36%.

After Britain and the U.S (N.Z. holds 80% of the American imported lamb market) Japan is New Zealand's most important trading partner. However, in January 1966 Australia and New Zealand set up a Free Trade area and as a result imports from Britain and elsewhere are likely to drop sharply: between 1956 and 1966 British imports fell from 57% to 38% of the market. The agreement covers about 60% of the value of trade between the two countries. New Zealand will benefit with large sales of timber, newsprint, pulp, lamb, pork, cheese and vegetables. New Zealand will provide a good market for Australian manufactured goods. Closer industrial integration between the two countries can be expected.

Recently New Zealand set up its 10th natural scenic reserve —Mount Aspiring National Park—which straddles some of the southernmost mountains of the spectacular Southern Alps. The total area of New Zealand national parkland is now 5,065m acres. The country has enormous tourist potential but its remoteness makes tourism difficult to exploit.

151

NICARAGUA

57,000 sq m. Pop. 1·7m. Cotton and cotton-seed now account for more than half Nicaragua's exports and late in 1965 the government established a commission to promote cultivation, marketing and processing of cotton. Mills are being modernised and new storage depots built. Despite the success of cotton, greater agricultural diversification is needed and the Inter-American Development Bank has made large loans. Each year since 1964 about 100 new factories have started business. Main industries are fertilisers, insecticides, formica, kenaf bags, textiles, dried milk, assembly of refrigerators, agricultural machinery and equipment. Chief overseas trade links are with Russia and Nationalist China.

NIGERIA

356,669 sq m. Pop. 57m. The two military coups which took place in 1966 were purely political and have had little effect on the economy of the country, so it can find no discussion here. Economically, Nigeria has been stable and could expand. By 1970 the country should be earning £250m a year from oil; methane should bring in another £10m. Oil will certainly be Nigeria's principal export for years to come, though cocoa, groundnuts, palm oil, tin and rubber are important earners. At the end of 1965 a new refinery came into operation at Port Harcourt. Gas is being used to generate electricity in the Mid-West Region at the new power station at Ughelli. Nigeria is associated with the European Common Market and makes large sales to Germany and Holland especially. Even so, Britain remains Nigeria's best customer and principal supplier, though the position may change as Nigeria develops her trade with the Six.

NORTHERN IRELAND

5,451 sq m. Pop. 1·4m. To attract new industry the Northern Ireland government is carrying out the most extensive programme of factory building it has so far undertaken. Further industrialism is essential if the high unemployment rate is to be reduced. In 1965 12 new factories were completed and another 20 were completed by the end of 1966. Swedish, German, Swiss and Japanese industrialists are interested in Northern Ireland as a manufacturing centre, the first three mainly because of labour shortages in their own countries, the Japanese because Northern Ireland would be a convenient base for European distribution. It seems likely that the fall in employment in Northern Ireland's two oldest industries, shipbuilding and linen manufacture, will soon find compensation in new industries, which will be mostly light engineering.

NORWAY

125,183 sq m. Pop. 3·7m. Norway has had a slack period and many industries are either static or are declining. However, the government (elected September 1965) hopes to increase the national income by 20% by 1969, with shipping contributing 18% to the rise in output, other service industries 37% and manufacturing, mining and HEP 33%. Norway will need to borrow heavily abroad. The British Trade Promotion Fair in May 1966, called "Britain '66", was the largest ever held in Norway in an effort to re-establish Britain as a major Norwegian supplier. Britain has fallen behind her two main rivals, Denmark and Sweden.

Norway has established a Geological Research centre in Trondheim, two Fishery Research Institutes in Bergen, and a large centre for the Pulp and Paper Research Institute.

NUCLEAR POWER

Throughout Europe there is intense competition over a £200m-a-year market for power reactors. European countries have decided for the future to invest more in nuclear power than in any other means of producing electricity and are making major purchases of equipment. The main sellers are Britain, Germany, France, Sweden and the U.S. The Common Market countries get only 1·5% of their power from the atom, but this output will be trebled by 1968 by plants now under construction. France, the Continent's biggest investor in atomic power, intends to increase generating capacity 10-fold by 1970. The EEC nuclear authority, Euratom, predicts that by 1980 the Six will be producing 280 billion kilowatt-hours of electricity—70% as much as they now get from all power sources. A combination of improved reactors and lower-cost uranium has made nuclear power competitive with conventional power; in fact, in many parts of Europe it is the cheapest form of electricity. Even Switzerland and Sweden are planning to build nuclear plants because they are running out of water sources.

Many large deals have been negotiated in Europe—and the plants are equally large; two to be built in Belgium and in Italy will each cost more than £35m. Other plants are being built in the Ardennes, southern Germany and Spain. Probably the most promising markets are in countries that want nuclear power but have not yet begun large-scale production of reactors themselves—notably Italy, Spain, Switzerland and Japan. There is also a large market in Eastern Europe, though the situation is politically complicated because an inevitable by-product of the reactors is plutonium, a major ingredient in nuclear bombs.

(See *Britain.*)

O

OCEANOLOGY

Two interesting underwater experiments in October 1965 will probably lead to even more interesting practical new geography in 1967. Off the coast of Southern California U.S. aquanauts lived in relays for 45 days in *Sealab II*. Off Cape Ferrat on the French Riviera six Frenchmen lived at a depth of 330 feet in their *Con Shelf III* and worked even deeper, 375 feet. The French experiment proved that men can operate even complex mining equipment at such depths and Jacques-Yves Cousteau, the pioneering underwater explorer who organised the expedition, claims that his underwater building—two storeys high—is ready for commercial use in offshore oil operations.

OIL

(See country headings, e.g. Nigeria, for other information)

Oil is an ever-changing, ever-progressing industry and it is virtually impossible to keep up with all developments. On a world scale more money is spent on oil search than on any other commercial industry, except perhaps irrigation. (Refer to map.)

Alaska. An important discovery of oil is being developed in Cook Inlet, 60 miles from Anchorage. Conditions are hazardous. The well is in 125 feet of water and the drilling rig has to withstand 30-foot tides and 8-knot currents.

Argentina. The country's proven oil reserves have risen four-fold in recent years and there is a considerable refining capacity. In mid-1966 its capacity was 21m tons. In developing these resources Argentina has also carried out some exceptional works. It has the biggest pipeline project in South America—the 1,100 mile gas line running from fields in the extreme north to Buenos Aires. An oil line runs for 900 miles of the same route. Another line is planned to run an even longer distance south to fields at Comodoro and Cañadon Seco.

Canada. The most outstanding Canadian discovery of recent years, the Mitsue field in the Lesser Slave Lake area, is undergoing rapid development and already 75 wells have been sunk. Two other fields have been found in the same region—Nipiso and Kinuso. Already a line is being laid to link the former with the Mitsue-Edmonton pipeline. Still further north in the Rainbow Lake region, about 400 miles north-west of Edmonton, another important find has been made recently. One of the most interesting scenes of present exploration is in the Arctic Islands off Canada's north-east coast. If oil is found here it could be transported by water either to the St. Lawrence area or across the Atlantic to Europe.

North Sea. Tremendous publicity has been given to oil and gas search in the North Sea, where 12 drilling platforms are operating in the British section alone. Supply bases have been built at Sunderland, Hartlepool, Middlesbrough, Great Yarmouth, Lowestoft and Aberdeen. The search in the North Sea has brought many orders for rigs to the shipyards of Britain. The promising finds made in the North Sea indicate that before long gas and oil will become profitable here, even though the cost of drilling a single well may be as much as £1m—without a strike. Britain has great need of oil closer to home and less liable to disruption by political disturbances abroad. It is

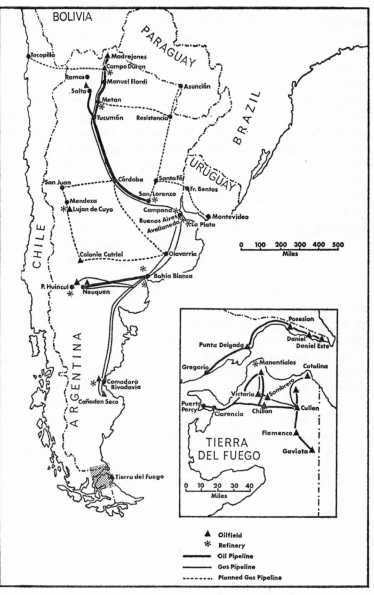

**GAS AND OIL PIPELINES IN ARGENTINA AND
TIERRA DEL FUEGO**

calculated that the value of retained imports will rise from £484m in 1964 to more than £600m in 1970.

U.S.A. In a recently published appraisal of the petroleum industry in the U.S., the Department of the Interior revealed that oil and natural gas together produce 75% of all U.S. energy. The industry directly employs 1·25m people. The U.S. remains the world's largest oil producer, but her demand for oil has increased so rapidly that she now imports about 20% of her annual needs, notably from Canada and Venezuela. Nearly 30 of the states produce oil, but 7 supply 85% of the oil and 90% of the methane. Despite the volume of petroleum consumed—petrol accounts for more than 40% of all U.S. oil demand—it is estimated that American fields could yield at least 1½ times the volume of oil so far discovered.

Other countries where oil from new fields has been brought into production since 1965 or will be produced by the end of 1967 are: Bulgaria (in the sea); Hungary (Tape), Spain (Tozo), Soviet Union (between Kama and Belaya rivers, also in south Ukraine and Kazakhstan), India (Gujarat), Israel (Nir Am), Saudi Arabia (Berri), Algeria (Ouargla and elsewhere), Libya (Serir, Umm Farud, Jebel and other desert locations), Egypt, (offshore, south-east of Suez), Tunisia (near Algerian border), Bolivia (Caranda), Brazil (Carmopolis and in Maranhão State).

Oil By-Products. Oil has something like 5,000 uses and others are constantly being discovered. An experimental station is at work at Lavera, near Marseilles, turning oil into protein. Large-scale experiments on feeding chickens with this product have been successful. A protein-producing works is being added to the Nigerian refinery at Port Harcourt. The protein processed there could be used, among other things, as feed at fish farms.

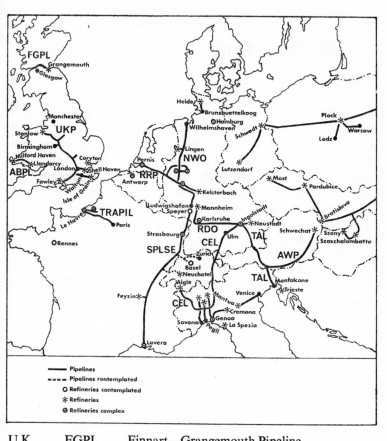

U.K.	FGPL	Finnart—Grangemouth Pipeline
	UKP	United Kingdom Pipeline
	ABPL	Angle Bay Pipeline (*from Angle Bay to the BP refinery at Llandarcy*)
Europe	TRAPIL	Transports Petroliers par Pipe-Line (*Products Pipeline Le Havre-Paris*)
	RRP	Rotterdam Rijn Pipeline
	NWO	Nord West Oelleitung
	SPLSE	Société du Pipe-Line Sud-European
	RDO	Rhine Donau Oelleitung
	CEL	Central European Line
	TAL	Trans-Alpine Pipeline
	AWP	Adria-Wien Pipeline

EUROPEAN OIL PIPELINES

OIL PIPELINES

(See sketch maps.) Since 1953 1,700 miles of large diameter crude oil pipelines have been laid in Europe and preparations are under way to lay another 500 miles before the end of 1967. The U.S. has 200,000 miles of oil pipeline. It is estimated that at any one time a total of 1000 miles of line are under construction in various parts of the world. There is great scope for improving the size, efficiency and potential of pipelines for moving large consignments of both crude and finished products. New methods and materials—including use of aluminium and plastics—would enable the diameter of large trunklines to go well beyond the present 41 inches. There is now a travelling pipe-mill, producing pipe "on the job" in long continuous lengths.

(The maps of oil pipelines are based on information supplied by the Petroleum Information Bureau, to whom the author is grateful.)

P

PAKISTAN

West, 310,403 sq m.; East, 55,126 sq m. Pop. 101m. Despite rapid industrial expansion, Pakistan's economy is still dominated by agriculture, which employs three-quarters of the population, and accounts for more than 50% of the national production and 90% of exports. Agriculture is not only still backward, it is bedevilled by flooding in East Pakistan and waterlogging and soil salinity in the West. Despite all problems, in the period 1966–70 cereal output should have increased 30% (to 21·5m bushels); sugar cane by 33% (to 28m tons); cotton by 5% (to 3·5m bales) and jute by 30% (to 8m bales).

Pakistan is trying to establish industries, particularly those producing industrial chemicals, electrical goods, fertilisers, paints, cement, petrochemicals, refined sugar and vegetable oils. The position with jute is interesting, for Pakistan is now not only the major raw jute producer but the leading manufacturer of jute products (Britain is second). The Adamjee Company produces a third of Pakistan's jute goods. In an industrial complex near Dacca more than 20,000 Adamjee workers produce 72m bags and 90m square yards of cloth annually. Nearby a new factory has been opened to produce from jute stems.

West Pakistan is making intensive efforts to improve its power supply. With the help of a large loan from the World Bank the natural gas field at Sui has been linked to an industrial centre 313 miles away. A high tension network capable of carrying 220,000 volts is being built with funds provided by West Germany.

161

The new capital of Pakistan, Islamabad, already has a population of 55,000, but the project is so vast that at least another 10 years will be needed to complete it. West Germany has supplied the water-purifying plant, which commenced operations early in 1967.

PANAMA

39,890 sq m. Pop. 1·25m. Banana, shrimp and petroleum exports have increased slightly. The only industry growing in importance is food-processing. The Inter-American Development Bank is to lend £3m for the development of the La Villa River Basin and for irrigation.

PAPUA AND NEW GUINEA

(Australian territory, distinct from Indonesian West Irian, formerly Dutch New Guinea.) Papua 90,540 sq m. Trust Territory of New Guinea, 93,000 sq m. Pop. About 2m. The economy of this large region is changing rapidly, with increased emphasis on timber, tea, mining and manufacturing. The older mainstays of the economy, copra, rubber, bananas and gold, are as important as ever but diversification is the keynote. In May 1965 the Australian government approved a Five-Year Development Plan costing £A300m for Papua and New Guinea.

PARAGUAY

157,000 sq m. Pop. 2m. More than half the land area of Paraguay is forest-covered but so far only a third of the region is exploited. Now, however, Paraguay is embarking on a scheme to develop its timber industries. Industry generally is on a small scale, but is rising noticeably. The formidable development obstacles of poor transport and lack of electric power are being surmounted. A new road into the Chaco region helps to bring cattle to export centres and roads are being built to the Brazilian border to link the country with Brazilian ports. A large HEP station is being built on the Acaray River: this will help industry. Agriculturally and pastorally Paraguay is improving: meat production should double before 1976.

PEACE CORPS

In their own unique way the world's various peace corps—groups of mainly young people working in the less developed countries—are making their mark on human and economic geography. The U.S. Peace Corps is the largest in the field, but 45 nations now have similar groups. Britain's Voluntary Service Overseas and West Germany's Deutscher Entwicklungdienst (German Development Service) and France's Volontaires du Progrès are other leading groups.

PERU

514,059 sq m. Pop. 12m. There is probably more new geography in Peru than in any other South or Central American country. The development that has taken place in a few years is remarkable. The fishmeal industry is the dominant trade and in 1964 made Peru the world's foremost fishing nation—with one-sixth of the catch—though it did not hold this position. More than 160 fishmeal plants operate along the coast. Almost all the catch consists of anchovy.

Today Peru is producing 250% more minerals and chemicals than 10 years ago. Mineral wealth ranges from antimony to zinc and the American companies that do the bulk of the mining are expanding. Marcona Mining Company will triple, by 1968, the capacity of its £7m iron ore pellet plant; Southern Peru Copper Corporation has invested £6m for improvements since March 1965 and Cerro de Pasco Corporation has expanded its great mining complex.

A factory producing synthetic fertilisers was opened in October 1965 and Japanese interests are building a £7m refinery at Callao. In addition, a company has been formed to establish an industrial complex, which will include a zinc refinery and sulphuric acid and fertiliser plants.

In the north coast iron and steel town of Chimbote the population has increased from 5,000 to 150,000 in 20 years. In 1965 General Motors opened a £2m assembly plant near Lima, the first of 15 American car firms which intend to establish plants in Peru. The biggest foreign "investment" however, is still American aid—about £30m annually.

Patterned on the old Inca aqueducts of 500 years ago, the water and irrigation projects involve moving water from the Atlantic side of the Andes to Peru's parched coastal lowlands by diverting the course of three rivers through mountain tunnels. On the northern coast the Chotano River will be channelled through 10 miles of tunnels to a reservoir near Chiclayo, where 200,000 acres will go into production by 1970. One of the largest and most important developments is the Tinajones Plan, in the province of Lambayeque, 500 miles north of Lima. A huge reservoir involving four dams is being built here by West German and Peruvian firms with Germany meeting the entire cost. The waters of the Rio Chancaya are to be taken through a very high canal into the reservoir, which will eventually irrigate 150,000 acres of near-desert land; 24,700 acres is the immediate goal.

Agriculture remains the principal occupation and yields are poor because of lack of modern equipment but far-reaching changes have been made. Under Peru's first Agrarian Reform Law, 1964, 17m acres of farmland have been re-distributed—at an initial cost of £100m. Some was taken over from big land-owners, and regions of government territory were thrown open.

About 18,000 peasant families have already been given land, but in some cases the plan has not worked and production has fallen off. In 1963 an efficient 511,000-acre ranch was bought by the government and divided among 14 Indian communities. Since then 100,000 of the ranch's original 160,000 sheep and cattle have been eaten, given away, stolen or destroyed in one way or another.

Across the Andes is the eastern lowland—the montana—which covers 62% of Peru's land area but contains only 14% of the population. It is rich in rubber, jute, fruits, coffee, timber and grasslands. But it is inaccessible: there are few roads and no railways. The government plans to colonise the montana by means of a modern version of the Inca highway network that interconnected the old empire. It will be a 3,500-mile span, hugging the eastern slopes of the Andes and con-necting with access roads pushing up from Peru's west coast. Already "penetration routes" have been made from the coastal town of Pisco to the mountain town of Ayacucho, from Nazca into Cuzco, from Puno down the rugged eastern slopes of the Andes into the southern montana. Cost of the enormous project will be about £150m. Scheduled date of completion is 1975.

PHILIPPINES

114,834 sq m. (7,107 islands) Pop. 32·5m. The Philippines'
biggest problem is the labour surplus. Every day 1,000 new
workers are looking for jobs: the population is growing by more
than 1m a year. In the past Philippine economy relied on exports of hemp, sugar, copra and timber for much of its finance.
Now, to make more work and to increase exports the Filipinos
are processing their crops, spinning hemp into rope, refining
sugar, manufacturing coconut products, turning logs into plywood and veneer.

The government is developing bigger and heavier industry
—cement mills, glass and ceramic plants, chemicals and metal
works including two steel mills in production. Mining output
has doubled since 1945. The textile industry can now meet
local demand, cutting down imports.

HEP has limited potential in a country of islands and as
there is no other major local source of energy Philippine industry is running on oil: 3·5m tons of it are processed by local
refineries every year to supply 90% of the country's power
needs.

At least another 4,000 sq m. of country could be cultivated,
and since 1964 some progress has been made with irrigation.
Fifteen mines produce gold and silver, 27 other metals including copper, zinc and lead.

The Philippines' main trading partner is the U.S. but West
Germany provides substantial aid and German specialists are
working there, especially in farming and forestry, as part of
the development aid programme.

POLAND

121,000 sq m. Pop. 31·5m. This country's growing industrialisation is shown by the number of people employed in industry —63%: in 1950 the figure was only 30%. Poland is the only country in Eastern Europe where agriculture remains largely in private hands, which perhaps accounts for increasing yields. Nevertheless, Poland has had to buy grain from the U.S. and Canada. Britain has a large trade deficit with Poland—about £25m.

POPULATION

The world's population is increasing by 200,000 people daily: by A.D. 2000, 6,000m people will have to be fed. The birth-rate is double the death-rate and 1·9 babies are born every second. The rate of increase in itself accelerating, so that in some countries—Brazil and Mexico, for instance—the total population will double in as little as 23 years.

The world's total agriculture could certainly greatly increase to feed them: for instance, of the world's 350m farming families 220m still use wooden ploughs. However, the "population explosion" is no mere term of poetic extravagance. A writer in the London *Sunday Times* on March 20 1966 noted that, "It is as if, in the space of the 20 years since the end of the war, the world has gone procreation mad." In the same month China launched the biggest birth-control drive ever made when the government announced that parents must not have more than three children. All the intimidation and restrictive measures of a totalitarian state are being used against parents who have more than three. Sterilisation is favoured and pressure is being put on fathers to undergo these operations. After the third child sterilisation is to be forced if necessary. Clothing and food will be refused at the birth of a fourth child and parents may be sent to labour camps; this is only one of many punishments. There seems to be little public opposition to the plan.

In Latin America the population is expanding faster than anywhere except Mauritius. In Venezuela the population has doubled (to 9m) in 20 years, compared with a U.S. increase of 39%. A former Colombian president refers to over-population as "the problem of our time". The growth rate in Latin America is 3·5%: food increase is only 2% annually. During 1965–6 the Alliance for Progress invested £500,000 in 30 population studies throughout Latin America.

The FAO, in a study of 13 Latin American countries, has recently reported that in only 8 is the minimum intake of 2,200 calories met—Argentina, Brazil, Venezuela, Peru, Chile, Mexico, Paraguay and Uruguay. However, many people in these countries do not receive this minimum. In the Dominican Republic, Colombia, Equador, El Salvador and Guatemala the average intake is well below the health-minimum. (The U.S. average is 3,100 calories.) Largely because so much of Latin America is mountainous, arid or tropical, less than 5% of its 7·7m sq m. of land is under cultivation (16% in the U.S.). Farming methods are primitive, too. In Venezuela many farms produce 2 bushels of corn (maize) an acre (the U.S., 67 bushels).

The FAO director, Dr. Sen, has stated that the food-poor nations must quadruple their output in 35 years to give their vastly increased populations "an adequate, though in no sense lavish diet".

For a long time Mauritius managed to amble along on a middle course—her standard of living low in comparison with Western countries but high compared with many African countries and Indian areas. Pre-1939 the population was growing by only half per cent per year. Then in 1946–47 malaria was wiped out on the island and the population increase shot up to 3 per cent per year.* The population is now approaching 800,000: by the year 2000 it will be 3,000,000—unless family planning is successful.

Percentage increase in total population between 1960 and 1970: Latin America 29; North Africa 26; South Asia 22; Far East 21; Africa (south of the Sahara) 16; Australia and New Zealand 15; U.S. and Canada 14; North Europe 7; European Economic Community 7.

In Britain, the rising birth-rate and the accelerated house-building programme takes up three-fifths as much open land, every year, as they did in the 1930s. Even so the current loss is about 40,000 acres a year. The U.S., with four times the British population, takes up at least 1m acres annually in new urban development. An area of "low density" sprawl in such regions as along the U.S. Atlantic seaboard is now known as a slurb—a combination of slum and suburb.

Places with the highest population density are:

Monaco	$\frac{1}{2}$ sq m.	20,000 people	
Macao	5 sq m.	188,000 people	37,600 per sq m.
Gibraltar	2 sq m.	24,502 people	12,251 per sq m.

There is no doubt that the population explosion is the most serious and most urgent problem that man as a species has had to face. For a full study see the author's book, *The Hunger To Come* (publishers, Abelard-Schuman).

* If preventive medicine were pushed hard in all countries the population explosion would become even more volcanic. This can be seen in microcosm by the experience of the suburbs of George-town, Guyana. Owing to DDT, infant mortality fell, in the years between 1947–9, from 350 to 67 in each 1,000: in seven years the population doubled and in 1946 it had redoubled. In Ceylon, too, at the present rate the population will more than double in about 25 years, largely because the death-rate has dropped by more than 60 per cent since 1945.

PORTUGAL

34,500 sq m. Pop. 9m. Portugal's economy is stagnant compared with the rest of Western Europe, except for tourism, which is expanding, especially in the Algarve region. Agriculture is so depressed and unprofitable that many Portuguese peasants have emigrated to France to find work.

There are promising developments in the production of wood, cork and furniture.

POULTRY

West Berlin has a 10-storey egg factory farm, which may well become the prototype of similar establishments in many countries. In the middle of a built-up area at Neuköln, the factory houses 114,000 fowls. All the eggs will be sold in West Berlin, where the market is enormous: the average Berliner eats 285 eggs a year. A British company sold the laying cages to the factory.

PUERTO RICO

3,435 sq m. Pop. 2·6m. This Caribbean island has a rapidly expanding population (2·4% annually) and few natural resources, but in the last few years has become very prosperous. The per capita income is the second highest in Latin America (after Venezuela). In 1953 75,000 Puerto Ricans emigrated to the U.S.: in 1966 the figure had decreased to an estimated 3,000. American investors are putting one million dollars a day into the island's industry. Sixty major U.S. firms have plants in Puerto Rico: in 1963 160 new factories opened and the total for 1966 amounted to as many. One of the newest and biggest plants is a £5m Ford Motor Company precision ball-bearing factory. Another is a major petrochemical complex that will export petroleum and petroleum-based products.

Puerto Rico plans a modernised fishing industry to compete in the rich home waters now exploited primarily by the Japanese. Tourism is becoming big business, with more than 0·5m visitors annually. Income from tourism is £60m a year and is the country's fourth-ranking industry. Economic growth is 10%, one of the highest rates in the world, but 200,000 more jobs will be needed in the next 10 years. It is unlikely that there will be any change in the island's unique (if rather vague) relationship with the U.S. as a "free associated state".

Q

QATAR

The economy of this small Persian Gulf Shaikhdom (pop. 60,000) benefited during 1966 from the new highway linking Doha and Dukhan oilfield. The road will also open up some interior areas.

R

RAILWAYS

Great progress is being made in developing international rail links. Each year the number of Trans-Europe Express trains is increasing. In these TEE trains customs formalities and passport examination are streamlined and take place while trains are moving. The latest development is the elimination of engine changes at the frontier. Until now Europe's railway network has been divided into four different electric systems but now these are to be unified.

The German engineering firm of Krupp and AEG., with the Swiss firm BBC, are developing a new electric locomotive, the E210, which will run on all four systems. The new locomotive will have a speed of 90 mph and its weight will be 84 tons. These new engines will haul trains between Cologne and Amsterdam via Brussels.

Another railway development has recently been announced. Leading European banks are considering plans to help finance investment of £600m in new coupling systems planned by railways in the Common Market. Half of this £600m would be available to German and French railways and the equipment would be fitted to standardise Europe's 45,000 locomotives, 105,000 coaches and 1·35m goods wagons. The new coupling system would allow the running of super goods trains hauling freight of up to 10,000 tons without any need for manual shunting and coupling.

The French government has allocated a large subsidy to encourage the construction of a prototype air-cushioned monorail. The first aero-train is to go into operation in 1967. The

government envisages a monorail network between the major
French towns with trains travelling at speeds of up to 250
mph.

REFUGEES

No aspect of human geography is more disturbing than that of
refugees. The crux of the world refugee problem has moved
from Europe to Africa. The mass of fugitives from Eastern
Europe has been absorbed into the Western world, but wave
after wave of Africans have been driven from their home-
lands by new political upheavals. According to the United
Nations High Commissioner for Refugees about 450,000
refugees are now to be found in Africa south of the Sahara.
Fresh movements are possible at any time in many potential
trouble spots, including Rhodesia, South Africa and South-
West Africa. Perhaps the biggest single group comprises the
150,000 Tutsi tribesmen who have left Rwanda since independence brought the Hutu tribe to power. The Tutsi
people are now to be found in the former Belgian Congo,
Burundi, Tanzania and Uganda. Uganda also has many thousands of Moslem refugees from the Sudan. Something like
75,000 Congolese have found sanctuary in neighbouring
countries while 150,000 people have moved out of Angola.
About 10,000 refugees from Mozambique live in Tanzania
and 35,000 from Portuguese Guinea have moved to Senegal.
The African governments and the Organisation of African
Unity have genuinely tried to tackle the problem in co-operation with the U.N.

There are, of course, serious problems elsewhere. In Europe
about 10,000 refugees from Communist countries arrive each
year. Cuban refugees arrive in Spain at the rate of 300–400 a
month and many others find refuge in the U.S. More than 1m

Arab refugees from Palestine are in the charge of the U.N. Relief and Works Agency. In Asia, the biggest refugee problem is that of the many more than 1m Chinese refugees in Hong Kong and 100,000 in Macao. Something like 350,000 refugees have entered India fairly recently from East Pakistan. India has 40,000 Tibetan refugees and Nepal another 9,000.

RHODESIA

150,333 sq m. Pop. 4·2m, including 221,000 Europeans. Rhodesia's declaration of independence is beyond the scope of this book. The geographical consequences have not been as noticeable as was forecast. Various trade restrictions have reduced Rhodesia's prosperity, but not appreciably. The world especially needs the country's copper and tobacco and if one market declines to buy these commodities another market will.

ROADS

By 1970 at the latest, Northern Europe will be linked with the southern tip of Italy by a four-lane motor highway. The decision has been taken to build the final section from the Brenner Pass via Bolzano and Trento to Verona. The estimated total costs of the 78-foot-wide section are estimated at 570m dollars.

More than 3,000 U.S. companies now do business in Europe and some, seeking to be independent in transport, are setting up their own truck network in Europe, though until late 1965 all made use of European road transport firms. In December 1965 the seventh largest road transport firm in the U.S., Denver-Chicago Trucking Company, bought a controlling interest in West Eurotransport Inc., in Amsterdam. This company operates in 10 countries and will probably handle much of the business of the American companies in Europe. Denver-Chicago is providing a rapid, door-to-door service within Europe and between the U.S. and Europe. It has negotiated trans-Atlantic links with air-freighter companies. Through its new company, Denver-Chicago plans to extend its service to Spain and Portugal and to Soviet Zone countries.

Road freight transport between West Germany and Finland is increasing every year by several thousand tons. Forty Finnish and 25 German firms have gone over to a system of exchanging freight trailers. Only the trailers are shipped, while the semi-trailers and the teams of drivers wait at the ports.

"The autostrada of the two seas"—Adriatic and Ligurian —on which work has begun in Italy, is to have 17 tunnels and 65 bridges on the 126-mile stretch between Rome and Aquila.

By 1970 at the latest and perhaps as early as 1968 a 7,000-mile all-weather Asian highway will link Teheran and Singapore. A road of sorts was 96% completed in 1966.

Brazil's Highway BR–14 runs for 1,350 miles from Belém to Brasilia through the jungles and scrub of Brazil's interior. Though rough and unsurfaced, the BR–14 is described by the Brazilian government as "the highway of dreams" and the means to a "new civilisation on the central plateau". The road is certainly proving its usefulness. Timber, rubber, vegetable oil, beans, rice, corn and fruit are now being carried on the road, which is transforming much of central Brazil. (See *Brazil, West Germany.*)

RUMANIA

91,600 sq m. Pop. 19m. Under the COMECON (Council for Mutual Economic Assistance) plan set up in 1948 by Albania, Bulgaria, Czechoslovakia, East Germany, Hungary, Poland, Rumania and Russia, Rumania was supposed to remain a primary producer, but she has refused to restrict her secondary industries and is building factories. Under her 1966–75 development plan, Rumania proposes to exploit her reserves of oil, methane gas, uranium and HEP. Much of the country's future prosperity depends on the way the tourist industry develops.

RUSSIA
(Soviet Union)

8·6m sq m. Pop. 228m. Because of deteriorating relations with Communist China the Russians have been intensifying contacts with the non-Communist world. Although 70% of Russia's trade is with Communist countries, she is trading more with Western nations. Main British exports to Russia are machinery, chemicals, non-ferrous metals, iron, steel, yarns and fabrics. Main imports from Russia are timber, cork, pulp, hides, skins and furs, metal scrap, textile fibres. The British debit balance in 1965 amounted to more than £70m.

Soviet-Japanese trade has tripled since 1960 and at the figure of about £135m annually is 10% greater in volume than Japan's trade with Britain. Late in 1965 it was decided to establish the first commercial air service between Moscow and Tokio, across Siberia. Russia has suggested that Japan should help develop Siberian industry by investing, over a period, something like £1 billion in oil refineries and pipelines.

In March 1966 when a large party of Russian economists visited Japan to prepare various deals the president of the Soviet Chamber of Commerce said that western Siberia had reserves of 40 billion tons of oil, 42 billion cubic metres of timber and vast amounts of iron ore, coal and non-ferrous metals. He invited the Japanese to help tap these reserves. The Siberian oilfields are expected to become Russia's biggest and for them Russia will need 4,338 miles of 48-inch pipe—41-inch pipe has been the largest to date—to run from the fields to the port of Nakhodka, in addition to about 500 miles of branch pipeline. They suggest paying the Japanese for the pipe and other equipment in oil. Russia has also suggested that it will buy from Japan very large bulk carriers of ore and oil if the Japanese buy the raw materials. They will buy equipment worth something like £40m to improve the harbours of Nakhodka, Vladivostok, Vanino and Mago. Also, if the Japanese will take some of the Siberian timber the Russians have offered to buy Japanese lumbering equipment and machinery.

To expand its business with Europe, Russia has made a very large deal with the Italian firm, Olivetti, which will advise the Russians on mechanising their huge bureaucracies and will sell them great quantities of office machinery. A Greek shipping company is to buy 33 Russian-built cargo ships. The terms include the Russian purchase of £10m worth of Greek farm products.

During 1966–7 about 120 major industrial plants are being automated, as a big step in improving industrial efficiency and quantity and quality of goods. Under revolutionary reforms introduced early in 1966 factory managers have much more freedom.

The Soviet Union is the world's largest coal producer, but targets during the Seven Year Plan of 1959–65 were not fulfilled. This has led to a shortage of power generally, though new HEP schemes on the Volga should help remedy this. Output of meat and dairy produce has increased but grain remains inadequate, hence Russia's large purchases from the U.S., Australia and Canada. In October 1966 the Agriculture Ministry announced that the wheat harvest for 1966 was 160m tons, the largest in the nation's history and 40m tons over the 1965 yield. The Russians have revealed that two-fifths of the labour force is engaged in agriculture. The government plans to double the output of tractors by 1970. Irrigation is to be expanded in the south and large drainage projects are in progress in central European Russia.

S

SAUDI ARABIA

927,000 sq m. Pop. 6m. Despite its size and difficulty of communications, Saudi Arabia is not the technically backward country it is so often said to be. The immense wealth from oil has given the country money to devote to various types of development. Transport and communications, irrigation, housing, sewage works and agriculture take the greater share of the development budget, but manufacturing industries are expanding as well. An important project is the £2m steel rolling mill at Dammam with a capacity of 45,000 tons annually. There is an oil refinery associated with a petrochemicals industry; gypsum blocks are being made at Riyadh and there is a large cement factory at Jidda. Salt-mining, flour-milling, soap, detergents, glass and plastics are other industries. Skins, hides, wool and dates are traditional exports. Britain, Japan and West Germany are Saudi Arabia's main suppliers. It is strange that the general conception of Saudi Arabia should be one of backwardness, considering the country's massive financial reserves.

SCANDINAVIA

(This is a somewhat inaccurate classification since this account concerns Denmark, which, strictly speaking, is not Scandinavian, and Iceland. However, it is a more practical classifica-

tion than "Nordic".) The countries of the Nordic Council
—Sweden, Norway, Finland, Denmark and Iceland—have
ever-strengthening ties. They have common laws for banking,
shipping and aviation and almost a common citizenship. The
Council has decided to intensify co-operation within EFTA. It
has also advised the Swedish and Danish governments to build
a bridge across the Ore Sound to link Malmo and Copenhagen.
At present motorists must take one of the car ferries over the
Sound.

SENEGAL

78,000 sq m. Pop. 3·2m. For centuries the people who live
on the banks of the Senegal River have had to watch helplessly
its destructive whims. During the rainy season—July–December—raging brown torrents eat away the banks and flood large
areas. In the dry season the Senegal turns into a thin, torpid
trickle and many of its tributaries become strings of stagnant
pools. Since agriculture plays a major part in the economies of
the countries through which the Senegal flows—Senegal,
Guinea, Mali and Mauritania—the river is a major problem.
At Senegal's instigation, the four countries plan to tame the
river. The Secretary-General of the Senegal Commission believes that vast areas of land now useless will become "a
broad, green fertile valley, with new villages, a highly mechanised agriculture and modern industrial enterprises". Huge
sums of money are necessary and the United Nations is supplying some of the funds. The first section of the development zone
stretches from the sources of the Bafing and Bakoy rivers in
the uplands of Guinea to Bafoulabé in Mali, where both rivers
unite in the Senegal. Further to the west, at Kayes, begins
the lowland plain where hundreds of miles of tilled land are
flooded during the rainy season. In future, dams are to protect

the flat land, while reservoirs will collect water to be used for irrigation during the dry season. The main barrage on the Senegal, which will also provide HEP, will be built at Bafoulabé. The project has only just begun and no date has been given for its completion.

SEYCHELLES ISLANDS

156 sq m. (92 islands) Pop. 45,000. In the last few years the islands have been facing difficulties. Copra production, the islands' chief source of income (70%), is increasing slowly but is being outstripped by the population increase. Also the number of workers in agriculture has decreased as a result of more efficient methods. The Seychelles government has been engaged on a full-scale land settlement scheme for small-holders. Cinnamon is the only other major crop. Prospects for fishing and tourism are being evaluated.

SHIPPING

Ship-building and cargo-carrying are remarkably prosperous industries, highly competitive and full of economic complexities. There are few branches of industry which are so sensitive to fluctuations in the international economic situation. The world's total number of ships (Lloyd's Register) is about 52,000. The 5,250 oil tankers represent nearly one third of all tonnage. Technically, the U.S. has the largest fleet, but at least half of its tonnage is in the "reserve fleet", and so U.S. leadership, by flag, is theoretical only. By ownership, the U.S. tops the list, however. Britain is the effective flag leader, with a fleet of 4,600 ships. At the time of compilation of this account only 10 were idle. The fastest growing fleets are those of Liberia (this is merely a flag of convenience, because of low taxation and other benefits), Russia, Japan and Norway. Almost all the flag of convenience tonnage is owned by U.S. and "exile-Greek" interests. Each year about 1,000 ships are lost or broken up.

EFTA countries account for 28% of world tonnage. It is typical of British and Scandinavian owners to sell their ships before they are worn out, and to have new vessels built to stay in the forefront qualitatively and technically. Thus, among them they have a full third of world tonnage built during the last nine years, but only 22% of world tonnage 10 years or older. However, EFTA liner tonnage has not increased at all over the last 6–7 years. For EFTA as a whole 42% of the fleet consists of tanker tonnage; for Norway the proportion is 53%.

Japan is, as is well known, the leading ship-building nation, her share rising from 28% in 1964 to 44% in 1966. Lloyd's Register shows that Britain, former world leader in ship-building, now has less than 9% of the market and is slightly behind Sweden. West Germany is just below Britain. Then come France, Italy and Norway.

In Britain during 1965 only 13% of ships launched were for foreign buyers, while 78% of Sweden's and 66% of Germany's ships were for export. Every major ship-building country, apart from Canada and the U.S., had far better export percentages than Britain. The British decline seems to have been halted, but no great improvement is likely because of slow building, high costs and unreliable delivery dates. Nevertheless, a 100,000-ton tanker, *British Argosy* (the largest ship built on the Tyne), was launched at Wallsend. Greenock Dockyard, Clyde, has been building the two largest banana ships ever made in Britain. At one time in 1965 the Swan Hunter yard at Wallsend was able to undercut 48 competitors, including some from Japan, to win an order for two 90,000-ton tankers for Shell. The first will be delivered in 1967.

Despite West Germany's own vital ship-building industry,

a Hamburg firm, late in 1965, ordered three freighters of 6,000 tons each from an Aberdeen company: they will be delivered in 1967. At any one time the seven major German shipyards have orders for 2·5m tons of shipping. The leading yard is that of the Howaldt works at Kiel, which is building a 132,000-ton tanker.

The John Brown company of the Clyde River proposes to build Britain's biggest shipyard, a project which involves diverting the Clyde. The shipyard might cost as much as £18m. The river would need to be straightened near the existing John Brown shipyard to enable much larger ships to reach the port of Glasgow. Diverting the Clyde would provide land to build the world's most modern shipyard which could construct ships as large as those made in Japan.

In March 1966 Esso contracted for a 152,000-ton tanker from Bremen, three 170,800-tonners from Kiel and two of 170,000 tons from a French shipyard. At the same time Shell ordered a 170,000-tonner from the Harland and Wolff yard at Belfast. In April 1966 Sweden delivered the 114,000-ton tanker, *Sea Spirit*, to British Petroleum. Big though all these ships are, shipbuilders are already talking in terms of 250,000-ton tankers, though some experts say this is the practical limit of size. A giant tanker is economical for several reasons. It requires a crew no larger than that needed to operate a ship of a mere 18,000 tons—between 29 and 45. The bigger the ship the lower the freight cost per ton. A tanker of 150,000 tons can carry oil from the Persian Gulf to Japan for 15/– a ton, compared with 22/6 a ton in a 75,000-ton ship and 30/– a ton in a 45,000-ton ship. The very large ships do have some disadvantages. They are, for instance, too large for the Suez Canal, and the North Sea is not safe for ships drawing more than 56 feet—that is, those larger than 200,000 tons. However, the Japanese can already build nine 200,000-ton tankers simultaneously and will soon be able to build a ship of 300,000 tons: they are undeterred by the supposition that beyond 250,000 tons a ship becomes uneconomic.

One of the most spectacular achievements of recent construction is the 150,000-ton tanker, *Tokyo Maru,* built by Ishi-kawajima-Harima for the U.S. Caltax Corporation. The ship cost £4m and is 1,006 feet long and is so automated that it requires a crew of only 29. Its construction, from keel-laying to launching, occupied 140 days. At any one time Japan has 8m tons of new shipping on order or under construction.

The Communist bloc countries of Russia itself, Bulgaria, Czechoslovakia, East Germany, Poland and Rumania have been building ships—and capturing cargoes—with remarkable vigour. The registered merchant ships of the bloc number about 3,000. As the age and speed of ships is of material importance in gaining cargoes the Soviet bloc fleets are favourably placed: most of the ships in the East German fleet are under 10 years' old. Russia itself is building large tankers and because its own shipyards cannot cope with the demand has ordered many from Japan. Finland has on order something like 150 ships for Russia.

The opening of the Volga-Baltic Canal means that the carriage of goods on the Persia-Baltic route will be exclusive to Soviet bloc vessels. Poland has gained a larger share of Austria's export trade and Polish Ocean Lines have a new service to Indonesia and Australia. The nature of the challenge by the Communist countries is formidable.

New techniques will no doubt include the use of aluminium, following a successful experiment. In the mid-1950s the Sauge-nay Shipping Co. launched its ship, *Sunrip,* 12,825 tons. By including 136 tons of unpainted aluminium in the superstructure the weight of the vessel was reduced and the cargo capacity increased by 220 tons. In 10 years the owners saved £10,000 on paint and gained £55,000 from extra cargo space. During the ship's life they expect to gain £170,000 as a result of using aluminium instead of steel.

Another technique patented by a German shipyard makes it possible to fit out a ship with several additional tweendecks within a few hours. This means that a freighter can carry bulk goods on the voyage out and, on the way home, unfold the hanging tweendecks and carry piece goods, such as cars. By the end of 1967, 32 German ships will be fitted out in this way. Sweden and Norway have many ships of a similar type.

Underwater freight ships are being designed in almost all the major ship-building countries. At a depth of 300 feet such a freighter can reach high speeds with a relatively small propulsive output. However, before the undersea freighter eventuates we will certainly see pliable tankers towing strings of pliable barge-like oil carriers, all designed to bend with the waves.

The unpredictability of ship-building can perhaps best be gauged by Portugal's intention to build the largest shipyard in Europe, yet Portugal has never been a serious contender in ship building. The plant, on the south bank of the Tagus near Lisbon, will be known as the Margaeira shipyard and will be capable of building ships up to 200,000 tons dead-weight. It is scheduled for completion by 1969.

SICILY

9,928 sq m. Pop. 4m. Eastern Sicily is becoming industrialised —e.g. a large oil refinery at Syracuse—with some rise in the standard of living, and even in the western part the standard of living and the employment rate have risen because of emigration abroad and to the Italian mainland. However, the west Sicilian towns are scourged by tuberculosis, trachoma, dysentery and Maltese fever. Agriculturally Sicily is still appallingly backward.

SIERRA LEONE

27,925 sq m. Pop. 2·5m. In a remarkable reversal, the economy of this country is moving away from its traditional reliance on agricultural exports and minerals now provide about 90% of the export earnings, a big increase since 1964. Diamonds are dominant and in an average year bring in £20m. A diamond-cutting industry is to be set up. Rutile mining commenced in 1966. Sierra Leone's rutile—it is used in making pigments for paint and titanium metals—is extremely rich, and the nation has the largest proven reserves—30m tons. Iron ore exports have increased.

Agriculture might be taking a backseat in earnings, but it does employ the majority of the population and intensive development is under way. This can be seen with bananas— 3,000 acres in 1961, 37,500 acres in 1966. Many foreign experts have been helping in certain fields. Formosans have shown the people of Sierra Leone how to produce two rice crops a year; Indians have advised on sugar-cane growing; British farmers have surveyed the country for development of cattle grazing.

Fishing is increasing—Sierra Leone has extended her sovereign waters to 12 miles—and tuna canning has commenced. Between June 1964 and January 1966 new industries established in Sierra Leone included a mineral-oil and a vegetable-oil refinery, a flour mill, an instant coffee plant, a brewery, and factories making shoes, cigarettes, paper and textiles.

The productive capacity of the Marampa iron ore mine has been increased to 3m tons of iron ore concentrate and the King Tom thermal power station commenced operations in 1965. Several industrial enterprises have been set up on Wellington Industrial Estate near the capital, the port has been modernised and the country's road network extended.

The country has embarked on a programme to make itself the major tourist centre in West Africa and to this end is building many roads. Britain is Sierra Leone's main buyer and seller.

SINGAPORE

224 sq m. Pop. 2m. The gross national revenue in 1965 was £112,002,000 and in 1966 was expected to rise by at least £8m. The two biggest revenue earners were liquors and petroleum. Singapore is not now a member of the Malaysian union.

SISAL

While present demands remain high—with the U.S., Britain and Germany the main importers—long-range prospects are dubious in the face of synthetic materials.

For 1965 the world output was 650,000 tons, with Tanganyika, Kenya and Uganda producing half this total. The Yucatan Peninsula, Mexico, where sisal originated—it is named after a port—is not now important for its cultivation.

SOIL EROSION

Erosion is still causing acute concern in many countries, especially Turkey, Iraq, Iran, China, India, Russia, the U.S., Australia and New Zealand. The position is, perhaps, most serious in Turkey, where the Tigris and Euphrates have been carrying away the fertile earth to the Mesopotamia Valley in Iraq. The big Keban Dam now being built on the Euphrates near Elazığ, eastern Turkey, is expected to stop part of the trouble. But further measures must be taken. For one, the peasants must be stopped from destroying the woodlands by cutting down trees for firewood. Lack of tree and grass cover precipitates erosion.

Intensive reafforestation programmes are under way in the U.S. and to some extent in New Zealand, where it was recently found that a heavy downpour of rain on loose volcanic soil cut a gulley nearly 40 feet deep in 24 hours.

According to J. H. Scott Watson in the *Agricultural Institute Review*, March 1965, an average of 13m acres are being lost to the world each year through erosion.

British industry and science is testing a new soil stabilisation technique, using a mixture of mineral oil and synthetic latex. It may help to solve many soil erosion problems. The technique was evolved in Britain and has aroused the interest of more than 30 countries. Treating soil with an oil-latex spray seals surface grains together and produces a stabilising effect, enabling crops to be grown. When used on slopes the spray stops rain washing away the topsoil. The system offers a promise of economy in time, labour and money in preventing some forms of erosion, but in others the cost of treatment would be greater than the value of the land. It would be ideal for coastal sand dunes.

SOLAR POWER

A French scientist has suggested the building of huge power stations using solar energy. He believes that to produce 60 billion kilowatt hours of electricity 100,000 parabolic mirrors with a diameter of 10 feet each in the south of France would be sufficient. Using this method, a sunny country such as Spain could provide the whole of Europe with electric power.

SOMALIA

288,000 sq m. Pop. 2·35m. This African state so far does not have a single deep-sea port on its 1,125-mile coastline. However, at least three large ports are envisaged. Two are already under construction at Shisimaro and Berbera. Plans are being evolved for the third harbour, at Mogadiscio. The main function of these ports will be to handle the exports of live camels, sheep and goats as well as hides and skins, which remain the chief wealth of Somalia. With Italy the main market for bananas—a record £3·1m worth were exported in 1965—the Somali economy is still closely linked with Italy. The Italians intend (in 1967–8) to help Somalia to develop kapok, sugar-cane, cotton and oil-seeds.

SOUTH AFRICA, REPUBLIC OF

471,445 sq m. Pop. 18m including 3·3m Europeans. Prosperity and progress is very evident, with a 5% productivity increase. The farming contribution to the gross national product is dropping with increasing industrialisation of the country, but it still plays a major role. Predominant exports are now in this order—gold, wool, sugar, citrus and deciduous fruits, maize, wine. About 90 % of the country's wool clip is exported: the weight of the clip approaches 300m lb. Severe drought adversely affected the 1965–6 sugar crop. The estimate for next season is 1·5m short tons—a record. Export of citrus fruits now exceeds 4m cases. A series of droughts has reduced exports of foodstuffs and live animals by 21%.

Production of gold continues to rise. The 1966 estimated production of 30m fine ounces is worth approximately £377·8m. However, the industry faces the problem of keeping costs down in the face of the unchanged price of gold. An extensive gold-prospecting programme began in 1966 and will continue until the end of 1968.

Britain is the biggest importer of South African goods, taking approximately one third. British exports to South Africa are falling, while the U.S.'s exports rise, but South Africa is Britain's fourth largest market. Significantly, West Germany holds about 11% of the market.

Many Communist countries are engaged in a busy trade with South Africa, despite an ostensible boycott of South Africa for its racial policy. Communist China is importing goods worth about £2·2m annually—triple the amount of a few years ago.

In October 1966 it was disclosed that South Africa is exporting large quantities of uranium ores and crude asbestos, largely to help pay for the massive reserves of crude oil it is trying to build up—615m gallons. The government hopes that such a reserve would make South Africa invulnerable to an oil embargo.

Under the apartheid structure, South Africa intends to turn the African tribal reserves into eight separate "Bantustans", which will eventually be granted full independence as nations. The reserves comprise 260 associated tribal areas and cover about 14% of the total land. They are backward, primitive and have few natural resources although 94 factories employing Africans have been built on their borders.

SOVIET UNION

I have listed matters concerning the Soviet Union under Russia because the word *Soviet* has unfortunate political connotations and because Russia is more generally the accepted name for the country. However, it is important to realise that Russia is not a monolithic structure but an enforced federation dominated by the Russian element, in turn dominated by the Communist party. The Russian ethnic element comprises little more than half of the total population.

SPAIN

196,700 sq m. Pop. 31·8m. Present-day Spain is hardly recognisable from the usual textbook picture. After years of decay and isolation Spain is the fastest-growing nation in Europe. Since 1960 thousands of new enterprises have created hundreds of thousands of jobs—more than 1m by 1967. Gross national product has increased nearly 70% since 1960. In 1956, Spain produced no motor vehicles: in 1965 it had seven factories and produced 170,000 vehicles. In Seville is one of Europe's largest textile plants, producing cotton and woollen goods. In Bilbao shipyards are working around the clock to make ships for many countries, including Poland and Cuba. Now that they have mastered the difficulties of building ships over 50,000 tons, Spain's yards have won big orders, including tankers of 91,000 tons and 100,000 tons.

As part of its development plan, the government has designated seven depressed areas—Burgos, Coruña, Huelva, Seville, Valladolid, Vigo and Zaragoza—as "growth centres". Firms setting up in these areas receive many benefits and privileges.

The city of Valladolid (pop. 158,000) is typical. From being a drab market town and railway junction, Valladolid is now ringed with factories. Seventy major companies are operating and have created 10,000 new jobs. However, about 850,000 Spaniards still work north of the Pyrenees and their remittances give Spain added foreign funds. Many industries are still protected by a high tariff and it will be some years before industry is in a position to meet full competition from more advanced countries. Much of the power for Spain's new industries comes from Aldeadavila Dam, the most powerful dam in Western Europe, which feeds a national power grid from the country's western mountains.

Targets have been exceeded in copper, aluminium, fertiliser, petroleum and cement industries. Between the Navarran villages of Orbaicetayn, Roncesvalles and Valcarlos a large deposit of copper and antimony was found in 1965 which should yield 10,000 tons of copper-metal a year. Much emphasis is being placed on better communications and recently a 10-year railway modernisation scheme began: it will cost £370m.

Spain desperately needs membership in the Common Market. Twice rejected from even associate membership, Spain is afraid it may be cut off from its biggest and closest trading partner, France. Italy has already tried to restrict Common Market imports of Spanish oranges. The decision to keep Spain out of the EEC is largely political.

Of course, the rush of farm workers to the cities has sharply cut food production, forcing Spain to import more food. The effect of poor results from agriculture has been aggravated by rising demands for food from an over-increasing population with higher living standards. (See *Tourism.*)

STEEL

Technology is revolutionising the economy and geography of the world's most basic industry—steel. Traditionally, steel plants once sprang up around the major sources of coal or iron ore. But today, all over the world, steel factories are being established by the sea usually hundreds—and sometimes thousands—of miles from deposits of raw materials. This is one of the most radical changes in many years. One main reason for the move to the coast is the recent development of giant bulk-carriers—up to 100,000 tons—of coal and ore. Another is the efficiency of the U.S. coal industry whose mechanised output now undersells that of German and British mines in Europe. Also, tremendous new deposits of high quality ore have been discovered in under-developed countries. The result is that waterside plants that are free of protectionist policies can buy raw materials wherever in the world they are cheapest, thus eliminating the traditional competitive advantage of a domestic supply.

In the Common Market, coastal plants now account for 20% of steel production. There is, for instance, France's big mill at Dunkirk and the Belgian-Luxembourg plant on the Ghent–Terneuzen Canal. Even unindustrial Portugal has a small plant at Seixal. The biggest plant will be that now under construction at Europort by 16 German steelmakers in conjunction with a Dutch company. This great works will convert 15m tons of ore from West Africa, South America, Canada and Scandinavia into 5m tons of concentrated pellets. The pellets will be taken by barge to inland mills. The saving on the usual bulk deliveries to the Ruhr furnaces will be at least 20%. West Germany's sixth largest steelmaker is adding greatly to its plant at Bremen.

While Britain handicaps its steel industry by excluding U.S. coal and Germany admits only a small quota, Italy has become a competitive steelmaker despite its lack of native iron and coal. It has achieved this remarkable success by relying on coastal plants, coal from the U.S. and iron ore from India, Liberia, Canada, Venezuela and Brazil. Japan's steel industry is wholly coastal-based, again with U.S. coal, plus Australian ore. Japan is the world's third largest producer and also competitive on world markets.

The U.S. has increasingly depended on foreign ore and now buys 33% abroad. However, this percentage may drop now that cheap methods have been found to extract iron from the hard taconite rock. This technique has been of great importance in the Mesabi Range region of Minnesota, where ordinary iron ore had been running out so fast that the industry appeared to be dying. Now seven companies are building 1 billion dollars' worth of taconite plants in Minnesota. The guarantee of a 300-year supply of taconite ore—which produces twice as much pig iron per ton as natural ore and requires less coke and limestone in the steelmaking process—is attracting new mills to the Lower Michigan area. For these and other reasons American steel development is the most intense in the nation's history.

Despite all these advances, steel-makers, especially those in Europe, have been expanding too quickly and world capacity is greater than demand. The European Coal and Steel Community had warned that this would happen. Britain will have excess capacity until 1970. West Germany has the same problem of over production and during the first part of 1966 had consumer stocks of 4·3m tons. Europe's chances of selling its excess elsewhere are slight and emerging steel industries in other areas are helping to create an estimated world excess of 17m tons annually. In recent times only the Italians have made significant profits. In cutting down steel production various countries, including Britain and West Germany, must also reduce coal output, with resultant unemployment.

SUDAN REPUBLIC

967,000 sq m. Pop. 13·7m. Cotton remains the Sudan's life-blood, although attention is being given to other crops. Large new irrigation areas, such as those at Roseires and Khashm el Girba, will permit further cotton expansion. New crops include sugar, tea, coffee, tobacco, oilseeds and rice. The World Bank, Kuwait, Sweden, Holland and West Germany have lent money for various projects. Industrial expansion is increasing steadily and many factories have been built. Perhaps the most important industries, planned or in production, are oil refining, fertilisers and paper-making. The government is trying vigorously to cut down imports by making many consumer goods in the Sudan. The general conception of the Sudan as a largely useless, barren country is inaccurate: it is a country of unexplored wealth and possibilities. About 120m acres are fertile, but only something like 5·5m are cropped.

SUGAR

The sugar industry is undergoing great expansion, largely because it is a basic ingredient of the many luxuries people can afford when their standard of living rises. Practically every sugar nation has been planting new cane and beet sugar. They are also building new plants for sugar by-products which include paper, plastics, tiles and hardboard, synthetic rubber, toothpaste, floor wax and explosives. Consumption of sugar is greatest in Britain—more than 116 lb per head. World-wide intake per head is 38 lb annually. New sugar exporters are Ethiopia, Turkey and Bolivia. Chile saves something like £7m annually by refining domestic sugar beet.

Makers of sugar mills are prospering. The four West German firms specialising in sugar machinery have large orders. India alone buys five German mills yearly. The Honolulu Iron Works, one of the world's largest makers of sugar mills, has sold many dozens of units.

In the U.S. sugar is being used in new and ingenious ways, for instance, as a substitute for fats in soap detergents and as car headlight-glass. Sugar is, of course, the universal base for alcoholic drinks.

SWAZILAND

6,705 sq m. Pop. 292,500. During 1965–6 Swaziland suffered the worst drought for 30 years, with consequent famine and loss of livestock.

SWEDEN

173,436 sq m. Pop. 7·7m. The main new feature about Sweden's economy is its rapid expansion in overseas trade, with exports (minerals, timber, dairy produce, precision instruments) and imports (cotton, wool, tropical products) rising about 15% annually. Common Market countries now supply 40% of Swedish imports, with West Germany alone supplying 21%. Sweden is a very rich market for foreign exporters: income per head is £730 (£489 in Britain). One of the most prosperous companies in Svenska Aeroplan Aktiebolaget, which produces the Saab car. Few people outside Scandinavia realise that Saab (company abbreviation) is also one of the Continent's largest aircraft and missile producers, and that it makes computers, weapons training systems and hovercraft. It has nine factories and 14,000 workers.

SWITZERLAND

15,950 sq m. Pop. 6m. It has been said that Switzerland is so stable that nothing ever changes, and this is largely true. However, Switzerland is perturbed by the number of its foreign workers—one third of the labour force—and has already expelled 10% of them—a mixture of Italians, Germans, Austrians, Spaniards and Portuguese. The watch industry continues to expand, but Switzerland has lost ground in some major markets because of intense competition—in cheaper watches —from Japan, Hong Kong, the U.S. and Russia. West Germany is now Switzerland's main trading partner, but EFTA countries are increasing their share of the Swiss market.

SYNTHETIC TEXTILES

In Europe synthetic fibres have become very big business, with more than 25 chemical-based fibre plants built or under construction since 1965. The biggest boom is in nylon and the expansion is most noticeable in Italy. Many companies are building plants in foreign countries—Courtaulds in Sweden, Imperial in Portugal, Holland's A.K.U. in Spain, Farbenfabriken in Belgium, Chemstrand in Scotland, Firestone in France and Du Pont in Germany. ICI research workers have produced synthetic sisal. The price at present is much more than that of the natural product, but it is expected to come down. This could seriously affect the economy of Tanganyika.

T

TANZANIA

363,708 sq m. Pop. Tanganyika 10m; Zanzibar 330,000. Many new commercial and agricultural projects are under way as Tanzania consolidates its position. They include textile mills at Mwanza, Arusha and Dar-es-Salaam; a sisal-spinning factory at Dar-es-Salaam (financed by Holland and West Germany); cashew nut processing at Dar-es-Salaam, Mtwara and Lindi; coffee processing at Bukoba; soap-making at Tanga; biscuits and radios at Arusha; and, most importantly, a £5m oil refinery at Dar-es-Salaam.

Sisal accounts for a quarter of Tanganyika's exports and Britain is the chief buyer. As mentioned elsewhere, synthetic sisal may later adversely affect Tanganyika's sisal trade. Africans are taking an increasing share in cash crop production— cotton, coffee, oil seeds, cloves.

Tanganyika and Zambia are insistent on a railway to link the two countries, in spite of a World Bank recommendation that a road would be much more useful. Chinese and Anglo-Canadian teams have each agreed to finance the surveying of a railway and China is prepared to pay the cost of building it.

The government's three main long-term objectives—by 1980 —are to raise the annual per capita income from the present £19·6 to £45·1 despite an estimated population increase of 30%; to make the country self-sufficient in trained manpower; to raise life expectancy from 35 to 50. Tanganyika is richer in minerals than previously supposed: prospects for development are important. A new rich diamond field has been discovered in the Singida district. The tourist industry is becoming increasingly important as a revenue earner in Tanganyika and Zanzibar.

THAILAND

198,247 sq m. Pop. 30m. Development in the north-east provinces of Thailand is remarkable. The recently completed (1966) 380-mile "Friendship Highway" with its 500 miles of feeder roads has cut travel time between Bangkok and the Laotian border from weeks (depending on the weather) to eight hours. At the same time it has opened up vast new markets for the north-east's cash crops of jute, tobacco and maize. The scope for new dams, canals, wells and reservoirs is enormous, but so far only 4,000 of the 14,000 villages have enough drinking and irrigation water. At least 90% of the people of this region suffer from disease.

The total Mekong Project envisages the irrigation of 963,690 acres by 1975. The present project is only the first phase of the overall plan, which will double Thai rice production, bringing it from 200,000 to 400,000 tons. The huge Yanhee Dam project, financed by the World Bank, should meet most of Thailand's demand for electricity, which is rising by more than 10% a year.

Mining, as yet relatively undeveloped, is making good progress. Tin, the major mineral, was previously shipped abroad as ore, but now all tin ore is refined at the new smelter at Phuket. Large zinc deposits close to the Burma border are to be developed, oil deposits in the Gulf of Thailand are being surveyed and lead, tungsten, salt, gypsum and manganese are being exploited. In 1967 a steel plant operated jointly by Thailand and Japan will commence operations with about 30% of its raw materials coming from Thai sources. This is only the beginning of what could be an important industry as West

Germany has helped to finance a survey to gauge the possibility of totally supplying steel mills from local sources. Mining and other activities will be aided by a new seven-year road-building programme which will cost £136m. Overall, Thailand's second Five-Year Plan (1967–71) will cost £650m.

One of the most interesting recent developments in this country has been the activity of the Bangkok Bank, which will soon have Bangkok's tallest building. Having increased its assets tenfold since 1956, the bank makes loans at 12% interest compared to Thailand's usual 25%. (Village moneylenders charge up to 180%.) Among the bank's most important customers are Thai farmers, whose rice and corn account for 42% of Thailand's export income and for 6% of the country's economic growth rate. The Thai government owns 30% of the bank's shares so it is likely to support the bank's insistence on crop-support schemes, such as repeal of the 25% export tax on rice.

Each year the port of Bangkok becomes more congested and engineers are finishing plans for a new port 100 miles down the coast from Bangkok, near the border with Cambodia. Much of the planning has been taking place at Delft, Holland, on a model of the region 250 feet by 120 feet. The main purpose of the Dutch study is to discover how silting of the Chao Praya River can be controlled.

One of Thailand's worries concerns the future of teak reserves. Teak trees have been overcut three times their permitted yield and some teak forests face extinction. Experts say that within 30 years no teak will be left in Thailand unless vigorous efforts are made to ensure conservation.

TIMBER

Contrary to general impressions, there will certainly be no shortage of timber in the foreseeable future because, apart from the existing natural reserves, the planting of forests is being scientifically carried out in many countries. The demand could rise sharply without endangering supplies, despite regional setbacks as in Finland. Indeed, it has risen. According to the FAO, in the last decade production of sawn timber has increased by 20%; plywood by 150%; wood-pulp by 60% and newsprint by 50%.

Because of the increased demand and the certain future for timber most countries have been planting forests as long-term investments. New techniques include the growing of cold and temperate zone soft-woods in tropical areas to reduce maturity period from 60 and 80 years to 7 years. About two-thirds of the world's forests have been traditionally classed as inaccessible, but with advanced methods many areas could be opened up. Britain has the smallest proportion of timber in Europe (about 3m acres), which helps to account for forestry products making up more than 8% of total imports. Between 1964 and 1974 the Forestry Commission will have planted a further 450,000 acres and private estates will have increased by 300,000 acres. The plan is for a total of 5m acres (about the size of Wales). However, because of increasing demand it is unlikely that the percentage of timber imports will drop. It will probably increase.

TIN

There is some indication that tin is slowly becoming a rare metal and experts in several countries are urging economy in its consumption until some substitute can be found for the use of tin in tin-plate. Britain, as the third largest consumer (after the U.S. and Russia), is particularly concerned. In recent years production has increased only slightly, but the demand a great deal, with consequent rise in prices. A great difficulty is that more than 75% of the non-Communist world's reserves are concentrated in countries of uncertain political outlook— Malaysia, Bolivia, Thailand, Nigeria, Indonesia, Congo. The Third International Tin Agreement, running from June 1966 until June 1971, may help to solve the various acute problems associated with tin.

TOBACCO

Despite heavy taxation, the tobacco industry is thriving. Flourishing tobacco monopolies produce 5% of the national budget in France (£300m annually), 10% in Italy and 15% in Formosa. Countries such as Egypt and Japan earn valuable foreign exchange from tobacco exports, which are also handled by state monopolies. Japan's Tobacco Trust employs 400,000 people. Bulgaria depends on tobacco for 10% of its export income. Taxes on cigarettes are highest in Denmark (90% of the price) and Sweden (83%).

TOGO

21,000 sq m. Pop. 1·6m. A few miles from the old harbour of Lomé, which is not suitable for modern shipping, West Germany is building Togo an efficient modern overseas port. The German government is financing the project and a German engineering syndicate is carrying it out. The 500 ships which annually use the new well-equipped port of Lomé will be protected from heavy surf and tornadoes by a breakwater a mile long. The sea is 55 feet deep along the site of the mole (breakwater) and enormous quantities of granite, brought by shuttle-service trains from 43 miles inland, are being dumped.

TOURISM

That tourism is one of the world's most rapidly developing industries is easily shown by figures. In 1965, for instance, about 110m tourists—the definition being people travelling in countries other than their own—spent something like £4,000m. The rate of increase is about 15% annually. Money from tourism is a significant contribution to the economy of many countries. Taken as a proportion of export earnings, tourism provides Spain with nine-tenths of her funds, Italy with a fifth, France a tenth, though this is falling. In the U.S., Britain and West Germany tourist money amounted to about 5%, a considerable amount when translated into currency—about £350m in Britain's case. Dividends from a flourishing tourist industry affect many aspects of the economy—catering, transport and service industries, for instance. Also, an exporter benefits by having potential foreign customers at hand and the retail trade makes a great deal of money. It is estimated, for example, that overseas visitors to Britain buy more than 25,000 cars each year.

TRADE BETWEEN EAST AND WEST

As mentioned in passing in several other entries, East-West trade is becoming more extensive and intensive, and rising by about 10% annually. In 1965 it reached well over £2 billion for the first time ever. Some of the deals are complex and politically involved. For instance, Japan imports large quantities of coal from North Vietnam; Britain buys cashmere from Communist China, manufactures it into woollen goods and sells them to the U.S. and other Western countries. Some of Italy's shipyards are dependent on production of Russian tankers. Several countries rely heavily on Eastern markets. Austria and Greece each sell 20% of their exports to Communist countries and Finland 18%. Russia is by far the West's biggest customer but never publicises its vast purchases. Communist China, Poland, Czechoslovakia and East Germany are the other leading buyers, while West Germany is the leading Western seller, followed by Britain and Italy. However, positions are likely to change at any time, with France—in a trade pact with Russia in 1965 France called for a more than 100% increase in trade—Japan and the U.S. aggressively seeking Eastern bloc markets. To raise the quality of their production Eastern bloc countries have been forced to form joint companies with Western firms.

TRINIDAD AND TOBAGO

1,864 and 116 sq m. respectively. Pop. 1m. During 1965, under government pressure and popular interest, Trinidad and Tobago's agriculture began a pronounced shift from its traditional reliance on the sugar-coffee-cocoa-citrus export pattern. Diversification is now the keynote, especially towards beef and dairy cattle, coconuts, rice and mangoes, poultry and pigs. Many breeding cattle have been imported from Canada, the U.S. and Puerto Rico. Crops fairly new to Trinidad and Tobago such as maize and sorghum, soyabeans and Irish potatoes, are being exploited. Industrially, the picture is changing, too, with several textile factories and chemical ferti- liser and cement works. However, the islands are still dependent on oil for their prosperity—85% of all exports. With an annual population increase of 3% the government is constantly worried about its decreasing oil reserves—they could run out in 12–16 years. Tourism is being encouraged. A new town— Trinidad City—is being built 10 miles from the capital, Port of Spain, and though it will not be finished until 1974 all in- dustrial sites have already been taken. Japanese are to make plastic pipes; a Venezuelan manufacturer will build a shoe factory. Britain and the U.S. are Trinidad's main markets, but British sales to Trinidad and Tobago have fallen sharply.

TROPICS

In the past, trade in tropical areas has mainly involved primary agricultural produce and mineral ores, but less developed countries need to establish industries based on processing of raw materials. One of the chief influences in developing countries along these lines is the Tropical Products Institute, since 1955 a branch of the British Ministry of Overseas Development. Through its "Small Industry Reports" the Institute advises governments and private businessmen of the tropics how to establish suitable industries. In recent months the Institute has been responsible for a match factory in Fiji, making of fibre suitcases in Sierra Leone, improvement of fish-drying in Aden, manufacture of desiccated coconut in several places. The Institute has several divisions—Foods and Drugs; Cellulose, Essential Oils and Pesticides; Economics and

Marketing. Considering that its staff totals only about 160, the Institute achieves a great deal.

TRUCIAL STATES

Abu Dhabi; Dubai; Sharjah; Ras al Khaimah; Ajman; Umm al Qaiwain; Fujairah. Projects under consideration or in execution include surveys of natural resources, roads, electricity and water supplies and improved agriculture. The Buraimi–Abu Dhabi water pipeline was completed in March 1965, providing an unlimited water supply for the first time. The Shaikh of Dubai is trying to turn his country into a commercial centre by attracting business with tax and tariff benefits.

TUNNELS

Mont Blanc Tunnel. This tunnel was opened in July 1965, but I feel some mention of it is necessary as it has not yet found its way into textbooks. The tunnel is the world's longest automobile tunnel, $7\frac{1}{4}$ miles. It has two lanes, air conditioned and equipped with radar traffic control. It shortens the road between Paris and Rome by 125 miles—even more when winter snows close the Alpine passes. Probably 1·3m cars a year will use the tunnel.

At the end of October 1966 it was announced that building of the Channel Tunnel would commence in 1969 and that it would probably be completed by 1975.

TURKEY

294,502 sq m. Pop. 32m. Without a heavy inflow of foreign aid, Turkey can make little progress. Its population is increasing by 3% a year, but agricultural production by only 2½%. Despite cheap wheat imports from the U.S.—total imports of U.S. farm commodities are worth £20m yearly—Turkey is still short of money for foreign purchases. Russia has agreed to provide credits up to £60m for factories making tractors, textiles and chemicals, for an oil refinery and HEP. The Common Market countries are collectively providing as much money. Tobacco had been for many years the leading export crop: now cotton brings in more money. Main industrial development is completion of the Ereğli steel mill (£100m) which is expected to save £18m annually in foreign exchange. The U.S. and West Germany dominate the Turkish market.

U

UGANDA

93,981 sq m. Pop. 7·5m. The economic geography of this African country has changed radically since it attained independence in October 1962. The situation during 1966 was that 14 major industries had been started, 9 more were under construction, 19 were decided and merely awaiting construction and 24 projects were being considered. About £17m is involved. (An encyclopaedia published in 1965 noted that Uganda "is mainly agricultural ... with some minerals" and gave no reference to industry.) Perhaps the most important manufactures are rolled steel and galvanised iron sheeting.

Coffee remains the chief export but to reduce dependence on this crop the government is expanding sugar production and livestock farming. Mineral production has reached record levels, with copper predominant.

Britain, China, Yugoslavia, West Germany and Russia have all given money towards various developments. The U.S. is Uganda's main buyer and Britain its main supplier. Uganda's prospects seem most favourable.

UNITED STATES OF AMERICA

3,548,974 sq m. Pop. 195m (including territories). The U.S. is a country of such geographical diversity and complexity and it has reached such a remarkably high level of industrial productivity that it can almost be said that, in a sense, developments are very few. Virtually every economic aspect of the nation has been exploited and while products can increase in volume the variety is more limited. The relative position of the various states in production of minerals, crops, livestock etc. remains constant. One of the few variables is population distribution: more and more people tend to move to the cities and to the states of California and Florida. The wealth of California attracts a stream of 1,000 new settlers a day.

The significant aspect of American geography in 1966–7 is not that taking place within the nation's borders, but the many steps the U.S. is taking to support other countries, by means of direct monetary aid, investment, free or cheap food in vast quantities, supply of material and equipment and distribution of expertise and advice. There is no doubt that world economic geography largely depends on the United States continuing to act as world benefactor No. 1. Without American aid the economy of many countries would collapse and people would starve. At least 50 countries are wholly or largely dependent on American bounty: this is one of the most remarkable facts of modern geography. Apart from complex government action to keep so many countries at a reasonable level of prosperity, American businessmen are increasingly concerned with foreign markets—especially in Europe. Since 1958 more than 3,000 American companies have started new operations or licensed the manufacture of their products in Europe.

In 1965 and 1966 American businessmen increased their foreign investments by 20% and the figure is likely to be the same for 1967. However, the U.S. share of European investment is still relatively small—less than 5%. U.S. investment is mainly concentrated in three countries—Britain, France and West Germany. In Britain U.S. companies make, for instance, 55% of the vacuum cleaners, 34% of the tyres and control half the nation's 400,000 service stations. In France, the Americans account for 70% of washing-machine manufacture, 40% of the rubber and 35% of farm machinery. In West Germany American firms are deeply entrenched in the motor vehicle industry (40%); oil refineries (50%) and computers (80%) Because so much American money is tied up in consumer-goods industries—household linen, razor blades, canned foods, for instance—the U.S. has a marked effect on everyday life in many parts of Europe.

The main U.S. exports are now (expressed as percentages of the total), machinery, 29; wheat, corn, food and livestock, 23; manufactured goods, 19; chemicals, 9; tobacco, oilseeds and cotton, 7; vehicles 6; aircraft 4. Main imports are: food and livestock, 19; crude materials, 15; petroleum and products, 10; machinery, 7; non-ferrous metals, 5; vehicles, 4; textiles and products 4. Britain has failed to hold its share of the U.S. market in competition with Japan and West Germany.

Shipping is one of the few aspects of American economy in a poor state. According to shipbuilders, more than 90% of American dry-cargo ships and 60% of tankers are past their economic life span. Orders for 100 ships a year in the past three years would have been needed to replace obsolescent ships. In fact, orders have averaged only 16 a year. Many shipyards have closed. The government is now paying 55% of the cost of building each ship and 72% of seamen's wages. Various regulations ensure that American ships have favourable treatment in carrying government cargoes, but the great majority of cargoes leaving American ports go in foreign ships.

The paradox about the U.S. is that although it is so wealthy and powerful it has many unemployed—about 4·3%. Yet many foreigners must be imported to help with farm work—Mexicans, West Indians, Canadians and even Japanese. In 1964 the law permitting foreign labour to be imported was allowed to lapse. At this time California had 0·5m men out of work, so it was assumed that the state could easily find the 70,000 needed to harvest the fruit and tomato crops. However, this did not happen. In California and elsewhere American labourers, finding the work too hard, gave up their farm jobs within a few days and returned to unemployment pay. Foreign labour is again being used. In 1965 more than 200,000 Mexicans crossed the border to help with various harvests. In any case, there has been a sharp fall in the agricultural labour force, together with rises in trade and manufacturing.

Building of factories, dams, HEP works, irrigation systems, port facilities, bridges and pipelines is continual in the U.S. but again, so much has already been achieved, that most new schemes are merely additions to older ones. The Minister for Agriculture said in 1966, "There is nothing new in the United States; we just keep on growing." This can be proved by the 10 billion dollars spent annually on dams, waterworks, sewage-treatment plants, water pipelines, canals and levees.

There is a nationwide surge towards atomic power in industry. More than 60% of the new generating capacity ordered by utility companies will be nuclear, against 22% in 1965. On October 31, 1966 15 nuclear plants were operating, 9 were under construction, 22 were on order and 6 were planned. That month Virginia Electric and Power Company ordered nuclear generators worth 200m dollars. However, because the U.S. demand for electricity doubles every decade General Electric estimated that coal consumption will double by 1980.

URUGUAY

72,180 sq m. Pop. 3·1m. During 1966 technicians from West Germany visited Uruguay to ascertain whether industrial expansion of the iron ore found near the Brazilian border is possible. This is part of the general survey of the resources of Uruguay, which has generally been regarded as lacking mineral wealth. However, it is now thought that marble, dolomite and baryta in the south-east could provide the basis of a reasonably important export industry. The "black sands" of Uruguay's Atlantic coast contain rare radioactive substances. Large oil deposits are possible.

The recent importance given to minerals is taking away some

of the traditional dependence on cattle, as the dominant source of income, and on sheep.

Also, industrial development is raising Uruguay's power requirements by 8% annually. Since it has no coal and as oil has not been exploited, water has been harnessed. The Baygorria Dam, built by a West German syndicate, has increased electric power by 30%. As a result, a number of plants are in operation, employing about a tenth of the population. In addition, flooding of the Rio Negro can now be controlled with the help of the older dam at Bonete.

V

VENEZUELA

352,051 sq m. Pop. 9m. By far the richest nation in South America, Venezuela remains the world's third largest oil producer and its largest exporter. Oil accounts for 90% of the country's exports. Production has reached record levels—something like 3·5m barrels daily, and still rising. An area north of the Orinoco River is to be exploited for further reserves. Oil disputes occur frequently. Twenty-five foreign companies mine Venezuelan ore and all too frequently the government demands larger royalties and part control over the companies' policies. In the Organisation of Petroleum Exporting Countries (OPEC) Venezuela has been leading a campaign to assign petroleum quotes in order to cut the worldwide oil glut and thus raise prices.

Between 1966 and 1968 no fewer than 360 factories will be built to reduce dependence on oil, although oil will be used in some of the new products; plastics, fertilisers, synthetic rubber, for example. Heavy machinery will also be produced in some quantity, with the steel coming from Venezuelan iron ore, the second largest export. Despite steady industrial development, (7% annually) agriculture still employs about half the population. Land reform is geared to a plan to make the nation self-sufficient in food by 1980, thus saving, at present, £65m a year in imported food.

Among the great development projects are: irrigation and flood control to bring 3m acres of cropland into production by 1980; airport, dock and road construction to connect backwater towns with larger population centres; an explosives plant (£16m); a high tension distribution grid to carry power from HEP projects in northern Venezuela to central and western parts of the country. An industrial complex is nearing completion along the Orinoco and Caroní Rivers. Many foreign companies, including some from Japan, are establishing plants in Venezuela.

VIETNAM (South)

66,281 sq m. Pop. 16m. It is not generally realised that France has large-scale interests here. She owns cigarette factories, oxygen plants, Asia's third-largest brewery and the Société Vietnamienne du Jute, which produces 3m sacks a year for holding the rice crop. Three French banks control 40% of the country's banking and about 100 French firms control the country's insurance, hotels, banking, cinemas and shipping. The country has benefited economically from U.S. military occupation and the capital, Saigon, is especially prosperous.

North Vietnam (63,000 sq m., Pop. 17m) is stagnant except for development in those industries supplying war materials.

VOLCANOES

Not all volcanic eruptions are listed here since most have been unimportant. One of the most serious in recent times was the eruption of Lake Taal, Philippines, in October 1965. In the centre of Lake Taal is an island, 984 feet high, which has its own interior lake, Lake Bonbon. The island of Taal is, in fact, the shell of a volcano and Lake Bonbon is its submerged core, the result of an eruption in 1911. In the new eruption two of four villages on nearby slopes vanished under a newly created lake nearly a mile long. About 1500 people died.

Vulcanologists have made a discovery about volcanoes following observations of the volcano that is forming the new island of Surtsey off the coast of Iceland. They have learned that a volcano can make its own lightning without thunderclouds. The hot plumes of steam and ash that rise from many volcanoes are often streaked with brilliant lightning flashes, which are usually blamed on conventional thunderclouds pushed up by the heat of the eruption. At close range, U.S. and Icelandic scientists found that great flashes often struck out of the volcanic plume, usually hitting the island near the active vent. Almost every time the scientists' instruments showed a strong charge of positive electricity in the plume just before the flash. After the flash the plume was neutral or negative, building up to positive before the next flash. This happened repeatedly without any cloud forming in the vicinity.

W

WATER

Professor J. R. A. McMillan, Dean of the Faculty of Agriculture at Sydney University, as recently as September 1965 warned of the serious shortage of water. Speaking to the Association for the Advancement of Science, he said that at the present rate of consumption world water resources could not support a population of much more than the figure for September 1965—2,500m. The world will have three times this number by A.D. 2000.

The need for water conservation, even in areas of regular rainfall such as Britain, is not fully appreciated. Industry has an insatiable appetite; 45,000 gallons of water are needed to make one motor car, 120,000 gallons to make one ton of aluminium, 240,000 gallons to make a ton of newsprint, 600 tons for a ton of synthetic rubber. Experiments in Australia have shown that to grow the grain for a single loaf of bread two and a half tons of water are needed and that one ton is needed for a fowl to lay one egg.

It may not be long before Britain and other countries need a national water grid so that drier areas can import water from wetter ones.

Of the 326,071,300 cubic miles of water on earth 97·2% is in the oceans; another 2% is frozen and useless in glaciers and ice-caps. The minute usable fraction remaining is neither evenly distributed nor properly used. Over the world the annual volume of water evaporated and precipitated amounts to nearly a hundred thousand cubic miles, sufficient to submerge the globe under 31 inches of water. But of this tremendous amount about 85% is fed back to the oceans; only a quarter, 24,000 cubic miles, falls on the land and two-fifths of this finds its way back to the sea. This means that the world's useful rainfall over land is only five inches a year.

Rivers account for 9,000 million million gallons annually. Only about 3½% of this river flow is diverted for irrigation and it is spread over only 1% of the earth's land. The remaining 99% of cultivated but unirrigated land uses another 3,000 million gallons a year—a fraction of what is potentially available.

The almost universal drought of 1965, the worst in recorded history, brought vivid emphasis to the need for universal water conservation and storage, and for further research into possible areas of underground water still waiting to be tapped. Hydrologists now realise that possibly nine-tenths of the world's fresh water is not on the ground, but under it. Vast amounts lie under desert countries such as Libya, Algeria, Tunisia, Mauritania and Egypt, as well as parts of the Gobi Desert.

In the course of drilling for oil in the Saudi Arabian desert about 56 miles east of Riyadh engineers have discovered large quantities of water—enough to supply the Saudi Arabian capital with drinking water for a century.

The total basic water supply available in the United States is about 515 billion gallons a day: Americans are already using 355 billion gallons of it. The margin is insufficient, for in the last 20 years America has doubled her water consumption and by 1985 will probably double it again. Obviously, many regions face critical water shortages. The situation confronts most industrial countries to a greater or lesser degree.

California is even preparing for its water needs in the year 2020. This is because the northernmost third of the state contains 70% of the water, while 77% of the water-need is in the southern two-thirds. About 29m acre-feet a year of northern water enters the Pacific, while the southern cities and farms must import 5m acre-feet each year from the Colorado River. By 2020 the population will be 57m (at present 21m).

Water

In 1965 scientists from more than 70 nations began to pool their research in the International Hydrological Decade. They have already established a worldwide network of hydrology stations to map climate conditions, to study precipitation, ground-water levels and stream ecology.

There is much speculative talk of changing desert climates. One scheme is to coat about 25 square miles of North African desert with bitumen which will reflect great heat, cause convection currents to rise which in theory would condense and form clouds, and then drop rain.

The principle works naturally with burning oil wells and forest fires, both of which often generate thunderstorms. The same principle is at work in the great French meteotron on the Lannemezan plateau in the central Pyrenees. One hundred great oil-fired burners around an area of 3,200 square metres can produce up to 700,000 kilowatts of power, a thermal capacity great enough to upset nature's balance. Under ideal conditions, the plant can produce its first artificial cumulus cloud in six minutes. The French scheme, largely experimental, has influenced other countries to build super meteotrons. In some regions a large meteotron could increase rain over an area of 500 square miles by as much as 30 per cent. This would make a radical difference to areas of outback Australia for instance.

One of the most interesting and cheapest ideas is to use the heat of the sun to distil water, especially as several deserts are close to the sea, and so combine plenty of sun with vast amounts of sea-water. The main problem is cost. The sun does not give concentrated heat and very large areas are needed to collect the solar energy. The cost of such an installation is high to the amount of water produced and it would be economically impracticable to use water so gained for crop irrigation.

The world already has about 200 de-salting plants producing a total of 100 million gallons a day, with many more under construction. The American company, Westinghouse, has built four distillation plants for water-short Kuwait: the plants now purify Persian Gulf water at the rate of 5,200,000 gallons a day. Other big distillation plants are operating in

Egypt, Libya, Saudi Arabia, Indonesia and the Virgin Islands. The largest sea-water conversion unit in the U.S. is at Freeport, Texas, which produces 1,200,000 gallons a day. The U.S. government is well aware of the impending shortage of fresh water and is spending 275m dollars on research and plants. By the year 2000, the U.S. government predicts, more than 7% of the nation's water will come from the sea.

Much of the money lent by the World Bank, the International Monetary Fund, the Inter-American Development Bank and other national and international agencies is for water schemes. For instance, the Inter-American Development Bank has given Brazil, Venezuela and Guatemala £10m to improve their supplies of drinking water.

The world has many islands at present supporting no population or a relatively small one because of lack of water. Already a major pilot scheme has shown that provided a certain amount of solar heat exists fresh water can be won at a low cost. The scheme was that which brought water to the island of Symi, one of the many Greek Aegean islands which have very low rainfall. The world's first full-scale plastic solar still makes fresh water from the sea at a rate of 5,000 gallons a day, an adequate amount for the 3,000 inhabitants.

The scheme is based on a system of narrow ponds about 250 feet long lined with rubber and black material to absorb the sun's rays. Each pond is covered with a transparent plastic tent. Sea-water is pumped into the ponds at night, then during the day the sun evaporates the water, which condenses on the plastic and runs into a reservoir. The water costs about 17s 6d a 1,000 gallons, compared with £3 3s for the same amount before introduction of the scheme. Most Greek islands, with their assured sunshine, will eventually have solar stills, with a resulting increase in food production and standard of living. Similar schemes on a larger scale could be used to develop, for example, the semi-desert of the California Peninsula, the desert valleys of the Rockies and the south-western states of the United States, the desert coastlands of southern and western Australia, south-west and north-west Africa, northern Chile, and many now unpopulated islands.

The solar still system will work efficiently only where sunshine is frequent and long, as in the places mentioned. Where this is not the case sea-water can be heated and sprayed into a low-pressure chamber, where a part of it boils into vapour and evaporates into fresh water. It is also possible to freeze sea-water and extract fresh water from it. In this system cooking gas is piped into a reservoir of sea-water. As the gas evaporates it chills the water and causes ice crystals to form without salt. When washed and melted the crystals provide large amounts of fresh water at less cost than the boiling system. The industrial east of the U.S., northern Italy, Britain and Belgium are among the countries which may well be forced to find fresh water by these methods.

A really big nuclear power plant—say 25 times larger than anything yet constructed—could turn sea-water into fresh water at a rate of 1,000 million gallons a day, at a cost of 6d per 1,000 gallons. Dr. Roger Revelle, a U.S. scientist, has suggested such mammoth plants, not for his own country necessarily but for the eastern and southern Mediterranean from Israel to Morocco. He foresees that this area could become as prosperous as when much of it was the Roman Empire, with a vastly increased production of vegetables and fruit.

Gibraltar is an obvious place for experiments in water production. One particular experiment, little publicised, could bring water to certain areas. The basic requirements are land at a height of about 1,000 feet in the path of a strong wind, blowing from the sea. At this height in Gibraltar two screens of fine wire mesh, each about 3 feet by 6 feet, were set up in the path of the frequent strong winds. Each square foot of mesh yielded a minimum of 7 gallons of water during summer—the dry half of the year—and 5 gallons during the winter, with an additional 8 gallons from rain during the winter. In practical pay-off terms, 10,000 square feet of mesh would win a quarter of a million gallons of fresh water annually, a valuable contribution to a chronically water-short place like Gibraltar. This is one of the cheapest ways of getting water, for after the initial outlay the only cost is maintenance of the mesh. The catch is better in summer because easterly winds are then blowing over a large part of the warm Mediterranean, thus absorbing more moisture than the westerlies which blow from the colder Atlantic.

In the eastern and north-eastern departments of France, in the Ruhr basin, in Belgium and Holland the water problem is disturbing. Not only are supplies diminishing, but the pollution is increasing, as in all industrial countries. The rivers of France alone pour 180,000m cubic metres of water into the sea annually: 6,000m are polluted. This is the equivalent of 10,000 trains each weighing 600 tons. The Rhine has become a gigantic open sewer from Lake Constance to the Netherlands. In the valley of Grisons, Switzerland, there are between 30 and 100 germs per cubic centimetre of water; at Lake Constance there are 2,000; downstream from Kembus the figure reaches between 100,000 and 200,000.

One answer to pollution is a scheme which has proved successful in the Ruhr. Though it flows through West Germany's most concentrated industrial region the river remains clean enough for swimming, because of the Ruhrverband, a co-operative society of 250 municipalities and 2,200 industries along the river. Whoever pollutes the waters must pay for cost of purification. The Verband has built 102 purification plants.

In addition to recovery techniques, another new method of water management is "recycling", an operation involving the use of water in a closed circuit. This technique is becoming increasingly popular in Germany. Papermills, cellulose plants, sugar mills, starch plants, fibreboard plants, ore-processing works, gas works and coking plants are equipped with or are installing recycling equipment to reduce the cost of water.

WEATHER

A scientist at the University of Miami believes that hurricanes, instead of getting most of their energy from condensing atmospheric water vapour, as meteorologists previously believed, are powered largely by vapour sucked up from the sea. The scientist told a conference on tropical oceanography that for every ounce of atmospheric vapour in Hurricane Betsy (September 1965) there were almost two ounces of sea-water vapour. If these findings are confirmed by further tests hurricane "treatment" may need a new approach. Instead of seeding clouds to deprive the big storms of energy from atmospheric water vapour, as was planned for Project Storm Fury for 1966, scientists may have to find ways of isolating the hurricanes from their principal source of energy—the sea. One suggestion is to cover large areas of the sea in the vicinity of a hurricane with a thin layer of chemical—perhaps of fatty alcohols—that would prevent evaporation and keep energy from rising into the storm. A solution of some kind seems necessary after the devastating effects of Hurricane Betsy, one of the most violent hurricanes of all. The southern part of Florida, as well as Louisiana and Mississippi, suffered great damage.

Droughts have badly affected every continent since 1964 and since 1961 the climatological services division of the Meteorological Office at Bracknell, Berkshire, has noticed a changing trend in rain pattern: less in the middle and high latitudes, more in the tropics. Rain-bearing Westerlies have also been blowing less frequently. The change was also seen in East Africa, where it was clear that the whole rainfall pattern had shifted slightly. It is too early to say if the change in pattern is likely to persist.

WEATHER FORECASTING

Long-range weather forecasting is one of the great developments of the last few years. The manager of the U.S. *Nimbus* weather satellite programme said in September 1964, soon after the *Nimbus* was launched, that the potential of weather satellites in long-range forecasting is "tremendous". Much of the potential had already been realised. Weather satellites were first used in 1960, when *Tiros 1* was put into an equatorial orbit. It soon proved its worth by identifying tropical storms: it spotted Hurricane Esther in 1961 several days before it would have been noticed by conventional means. But neither *Tiros*, its successors, nor any other weather observer had ever been able to make regular and thorough weather observations of the poles, where it is believed that major influences on the world's weather originate, or of the major deserts or the southern oceans. From its polar orbit *Nimbus* can do this. *Nimbus* can photograph every square mile of earth twice a day. Pictures from *Nimbus*' three camera systems can be used for weather forecasting by anybody willing to spend about £16,000 on a ground receiving installation.

Weather forecasting consists mainly of estimating the movements of depressions (areas of low pressure) and anti-cyclones (high pressure). Changes in the upper layers of air gradually work their way down to earth, but they take a long time to do so. Therefore, the more we know about what is happening in the air high above us, the better the prospect of forecasting the weather on earth. By studying a sequence of weather charts—drawn every three hours in Britain—it is possible to see how pressure systems are developing and moving. Methods of forecasting for several days ahead, based on large-scale patterns of upper air circulation, have been successful. Now, with the aid of the satellites, radio sondes (weather balloons), electronic computers to analyse information, and study of weather patterns recorded over long periods it is possible to make 30-day forecasts. By mid-1966 it was clear that these long-range forecasts were reasonably accurate.

Late in May 1966 yet another weather satellite was launched at Cape Kennedy—a football-sized one, compared with *Nimbus'* weight of 830 lb.

Remarkable developments in forecasting will follow plans suggested at a meeting of the World Meteorological Association in October 1966. There are plans to use artificial satellites to collect data from a network of automatic observation stations in remote ocean areas (on buoys), polar regions, deserts, tropical jungles, mountains and other remote uninhabited places.

WEST GERMANY

95,744 sq m. (excluding West Berlin). Pop. 59m. The account of practically every other nation in this book contains a reference to West Germany, a fact which emphasises the international importance of the Federal Republic. This importance cannot be over-stressed. It is necessary to realise in any study of geography of the 1960s, that Germany can claim the world's second highest exports (after the U.S.) and that its trade ramifications are even wider than those of the U.S. At the same time, because of labour shortage, a remarkably high standard of living and a boom in imports the country does have its problems. In itself, the labour shortage is indicative of Germany's industrial expansion: the number of vacancies is generally something like 675,000. About 1·2m of the labour force consists of foreigners, including miners from as far away as Chile. About 2,000 of them work in the Ruhr district..

West Germany's continuing economic success is due to:

1. Industry's assumptions (a) that to produce better and cheaper goods equipment must be improved (b) that sustained investment is the only way to increase productivity.

2. The realisation that competitive exports are the main method for increasing affluence at home.
3. Insistence by the public that price increases be kept down and acceptance by the trade unions that wage demands can only be justifiably made when productivity increases.
4. Enterprising and aggressive salesmanship abroad backed by reliable products, punctually delivered from home.

Government expenditure has been criticised both in Germany and by the EEC Commission. Much of this expenditure has gone on development gifts and loans abroad. West Germany is second only to the U.S. in donations of foreign aid.

Close to half the money allocated by Germany within the technical aid programme is going to industrial and craft training institutions and model farms. More than 400 such projects have been completed or are under construction in the developing nations. Germany's investments and agreements abroad are designed to bring about reciprocal preferential treatment. By assisting underdeveloped countries Germany hopes to gain essential supplies of raw materials at better rates. Again, many German factories have been set up abroad to make goods on the spot, thus saving the cost of shipping raw materials to Germany itself. The whole scheme is a masterpiece of planning and it is in every way successful. Having parts made abroad is also one answer to the labour shortage at home.

German technicians can be found in almost every country in the world. A German firm, for instance, has been building a rolling mill for double-refined steel at Ahwaz in the Iranian province of Khuzestan as part of the Iranian Third Five-Year Plan. A German firm has been commissioned to build a major irrigation project on the Cerro San Cristobal near Santiago, Chile. Foreign aid schemes are so diverse that they include a research centre in Nepal—set up on behalf of the Nepalese.

Germany has not sought to restrict foreigners building factories in Germany and hundreds have done so. In the Ruhr there are Japanese, Canadian, Italian and Dutch plants, among others. The Ruhr is today vastly different from the traditional concept of "Germany's Black Country", as it is still described in some textbooks. The Ruhr, though one of the most intensely industrialised areas of the world, is not black and its plants are not only modern but rival Swiss plants in cleanliness. Within the Ruhr are several regions where crops and dairy cattle flourish, without risk of damage from fumes or smoke, to supply local markets. In the summer of 1966 three villages were submerged when an artificial lake 11 miles long was formed by creation of the Bigge Dam in Westphalia, to supply water to the Ruhr.

Industry is extremely modern. German industry has spent £125m in 10 years in keeping the air clean. When a new power station, a cement factory or an oil refinery is built, getting rid of dust often costs more than a tenth of the total investment.

West Germany in general and firms like Krupp in particular are doing much business with Eastern bloc countries. The push to the east is based partly on new European trade patterns. The agriculturally protectionist Common Market keeps out Eastern Europe's traditional food exports, so that Eastern countries are forced to seek new ways of earning foreign currency. They hope to do so by exporting industrial products from new enterprises built in partnership with Krupp. For instance, Krupp will build a large synthetic fibre plant in Bulgaria, a cement plant in Yugoslavia, machine-tools plants and other works in Poland, Hungary and Rumania. Within a decade Krupp's trade with Eastern Europe is likely to equal its sales to Germany's Common Market partners.

Typical of German businesses is Badische Anilin und Soda Fabrik, which has spread over 1,580 acres at Ludwigshafen to develop Europe's largest single chemical complex. Europe's leading producer of raw materials for plastics and synthetic fibres, BASF is increasing its sales by about 18% annually. It has joined with Shell to build a fertiliser plant at Utrecht, Holland. It will build a great polyethylene plant near Marseilles and a £20m factory at Antwerp for fertilisers and synthetic fibres. It has several plants in the U.S.

Any relative deterioration in Germany's trade position—there was such a falling off early in 1966—is generally due to a high level of demand for imports and to both France and Italy having pursued deflationary policies which have resulted in reduced imports from Germany.

Expansion can be seen in every sphere of German activity. The Lufthansa Airline, with its new route to Chile via Jamaica, Equador and Peru, already flies to 63 airports on all the world's continents and is expanding still further. During 1966 additional flights brought new links to Mexico, Kenya and Russia.

Germany's efficient transport system is able to meet the needs of industry, in contrast to the position in other countries, notably Britain. Throughout Europe there is a 3,750-mile network of superhighways: 2,000 miles of them are within Germany. Since 1956 the autobahn network has grown by 625 miles. By 1975 it is planned to increase the autobahn network to 3,125 miles. When this has been achieved it will be possible to drive, without a single intersection, from Flensburg in the north to Basle in the south, from Aachen to Berlin and from Hamburg to the Austrian border near Salzburg.

The Rhine-Main-Danube Canal will directly help Germany's trade with Eastern Europe and the Middle East.

Y

YUGOSLAVIA

98,725 sq m. Pop. 19m. The government has been pursuing a policy of decentralisation and as a result the economy does not suffer the rigid control of other Communist countries. The most interesting development is a deliberate attempt to make industry competitive, despite all factories being State-owned. Tourism is one of the great hopes for future prosperity: it already brings in about £60m annually. It is hoped that tourist revenue will reach £150m by 1970. Because of the rapid rate of growth, inflationary pressures are severe and the dinar has been devalued from 2,100 dinars to the pound sterling to 3,500 dinars. The government has cut subsidies to expose industries to competition and thus make them more efficient. One result is that unemployment has increased and increasing numbers of Yugoslavs are seeking work abroad. The serious problem of divergence of living standards between the richer north and the poorer south remains. Evidence of Yugoslavia's confidence in the many reforms eventually being successful is shown by its application for membership of the General Agreement on Tariff and Trade (GATT) and for links with the European trading groups.

Z

ZAMBIA (formerly Northern Rhodesia)

290,587 sq m. Pop. 3·65m. (71,000 Europeans). The country is becoming more prosperous, with diversification of human activities. Copper, of course, is paramount and accounts for about 88% of exports. Production rose by about 65,000 tons in 1965. Tobacco, iron and steel, milling, cement, textiles and clothing industries have all greatly increased in productivity. A gypsum mine, capacity 10,000 tons annually, has been opened near Monze. Rapid development of agriculture is one of the government's principal aims. To this end, Zambia is being made self-sufficient in sugar by a fully integrated sugar scheme; that is, from cane to mill. Tractors are being distributed and ranching schemes and road improvements are under way. Tariff protection against competition from Rhodesia (prior to cessation of trade with Rhodesia following the political rift) and from South Africa has helped industrial expansion.

However, overlying the basic prosperity are the economic difficulties caused by the sanctions against the Rhodesian government. At the end of October 1966 Zambia faced economic collapse because of acute shortage of oil and petrol and a fall in copper production. The copper industry was being strangled because it was no longer getting coal from the Rhodesian fields at Wankie: a ton of coal is needed to smelt a ton of copper. Zambia brought this difficulty on itself by breaking the Rhodesian railways—a unified system serving both countries—into two separate systems, as part of the sanctions campaign. At the end of October President Kaunda announced a four-year development plan costing £400m, but at the time any possibility of its being implemented seemed remote.

INDEX

Index

Angola, 71, 174
Argentina, 20, 31, 32, 33, 68, 73, 76, 80, 156, 168
Armaments, 33, 85, 197, 215
Asia, 21, 32, 34, 46, 47, 54, 175, 176
Astronomy, 35, 36
Australia, 20, 28, 32, 35, 36–42, 57, 61, 66, 68, 73, 75, 76, 78, 82, 100, 109, 114, 119, 128, 130, 145, 150, 151, 179, 185, 188, 194, 217, 219, 221
Austria, 42, 43, 63, 83, 88, 111, 185, 205
Automation, 44, 45, 65, 178

Bahrain, 46
Banks, 46, 47, 51, 54, 66, 72, 80, 86, 101, 108, 115, 117, 125, 134, 136, 145, 146, 152, 161, 162, 173, 181, 195, 199, 200, 201, 215, 220
Barbados, 47
Basutoland (Lesotho), 24, 47, 48
Bechuanaland (Botswana), 24, 48, 49
Belgium, 23, 50, 63, 69, 73, 86, 106, 147, 154, 173, 194, 198, 221, 222
Bolivia, 20, 51, 130, 158, 196, 203
Borneo, 131
Botswana, (*see Bechuanaland*)
Brazil, 51–4, 70, 71, 91, 93, 132, 158, 167, 168, 176, 194, 220
Bridges, 54, 129, 176, 181, 212
Britain, 23, 32, 38, 40, 44, 45, 48, 50, 51, 55–9, 66, 67, 68, 69, 71, 72, 75, 77, 81, 84, 86, 87, 88, 89, 91, 93, 94, 95, 97, 100, 101, 102, 109, 111, 113, 115, 116, 117, 124, 127, 134, 137, 140, 141, 145, 146, 147, 149, 150, 151, 152, 153, 154, 156, 161, 163, 167, 169, 170, 177, 180, 183, 184, 188, 189, 191, 194, 196, 203, 204, 205, 206, 209, 210, 217, 221, 224, 228
Buenos Aires, 20

Bulgaria, 59, 60, 62, 63, 136, 158, 177, 185, 203, 227,
Burma, 60, 96, 132
Burundi, 174

Cambodia, 61, 80
Cameroon, 21, 70
Canada, 61, 62, 66, 68, 75, 93, 110, 111, 118, 127, 130, 131, 142, 147, 156, 158, 167, 178, 183, 194, 199, 206, 211, 227
Canals, 31, 62–5, 67, 76, 85, 92, 120, 164, 185, 194, 228
Canvey Island, Britain, 30, 141
Central America, 65
Ceylon, 27, 66, 119, 140, 169
Chad, 76
Chile, 20, 35, 57, 64, 66, 67, 74, 83, 113, 119, 120, 168, 196, 221, 225, 226, 228
China (Communist), 29, 31, 60, 62, 67–9, 77, 83, 93, 104, 109, 116, 132, 140, 147, 167, 188, 191, 199, 205, 209
China (Nationalist), 76, 152, (*see Formosa*)
Colombia, 20, 64, 71, 72, 168
Common Market, (*see European Economic Community*)
Congo, 22, 74, 134, 174, 203
Cook Islands, 74
Costa Rica, 48, 65, 71, 75, 76
Council of Europe, 77
Cuba, 77, 78, 149, 174, 192
Currency, 78
Czechoslovakia, 62, 63, 79, 83, 117, 177, 185, 205

Dairying, 21, 40, 65, 103, 104, 120, 146, 150, 151, 152, 178, 197, 205, 227
Dams, (*see Irrigation*)
Denmark, 57, 71, 81, 85, 88, 103, 153, 180, 181, 203

Index